SMALL ARMS
OF THE WORLD

SMALL ARMS
OF THE WORLD

General Editor: Peter Darman

Grange
BOOKS

This edition published in 2004 by Grange Books
Grange Books plc
The Grange
1–6 Kingsnorth Estate
Hoo
Near Rochester
Kent ME3 9ND
www.grangebooks.co.uk

© 2004 The Brown Reference Group plc

ISBN 1-84013-677-4

Printed in China

Editorial and design:
The Brown Reference Group plc
8 Chapel Place
Rivington Street
London
EC2A 3DQ
UK
www.brownreference.com

SMALL ARMS
OF WORLD WAR II

CONTENTS

MODERN
SMALL ARMS

CONTENTS

9MM OWEN

SPECIFICATIONS

9MM OWEN

Type:
submachine gun

Calibre:
9mm (0.354in) Parabellum

Length:
0.813m (32in)

Length of barrel:
0.25m (9.85in)

Weight:
4kg (8.8lb)

Muzzle velocity:
419m (1375ft) per second

Feed:
33-round detachable box magazine (680–700rpm)

The Machine Carbine, 9mm Owen was a submachine gun designed by Lt Evelyn Owen, and entered production at Newcastle, New South Wales, in the course of November 1940. The weapon remained in production until September 1944, by which time some 45,000 guns had been produced. In service, the Owen soon showed itself to be a reliable and effective, and therefore popular, weapon. The bolt was protected against water, mud and dirt, which was a decided boon in the conditions prevalent in the Pacific theatres in which Australian troops fought, and in basic construction the weapon was very sturdy.

The feature that most easily differentiated the Owen from other submachine guns of the period was its vertical overhead magazine, a feature that provided for reliable feed and also made it easier for troops to use when lying on the ground. There were three primary variants of the Owen submachine gun: the Owen Mk I/42 was identifiable by the cooling fins on its barrel, the Owen Mk I/43 (specification at left) that was lightened by the omission of the cooling fins, and the Owen Mk I/44 that could be fitted with a bayonet. All three variants had an easily changed barrel secured by a quick-release plunger. There was also an Owen Mk II version, but this did not enter production.

MG 1907/12

The first Schwarzlose machine guns were manufactured during 1905 by the Steyr company in what was then the Austro-Hungarian Empire. Unique in being the only machine gun based on the retarded blow-back operating system, the Schwarzlose was very heavy and was sturdily constructed, and as a result of the operating system had only a comparatively short barrel generally fitted with a conical flash hider. The weapon was so over-engineered that many of its components seemed never to need replacement, and on the outbreak of World War II in 1939 large numbers of these weapons were still in service in many parts of Europe. Reliable operation of the earlier models was dependant on the use of oiled cartridges, but the need for this aspect was later eliminated, and the Schwarzlose appeared in many forms. The main variants were the Maschinengewehr Modelle 07 and the 08, but these were later brought up to the same standard as the MG 07/12. Variants (with revised designation when drafted into German service) in service during 1939 were the Austrian 8mm MG Modell 07/12 (s MG 7/12[oe]), Bulgarian 8mm, Dutch 7.9mm Mitrailleur M08 (s MG 241[h]), Mitrailleur M08/13 (s MG 242[h]) and Mitrailleur M08/15 (s MG 244[h]), Greek 6.5mm M12 (s MG 202[g]), Hungarian 8mm 07/12 (7/31), Italian 8mm 07/12 (s MG 267[i]), Romanian 6.5mm 07/12 and Yugoslav 7.9mm Mitralez M07/12S (s MG 247[j]).

SPECIFICATIONS

MG 1907/12

Type:
heavy water-cooled machine gun

Calibre:
8mm (0.315in)

Length:
1.066m (42in)

Length of barrel:
0.526m (20.75in)

Weight:
19.9kg (44lb) for gun and 19.8kg (43.75lb) for tripod

Muzzle velocity:
620m (2034ft) per second

Feed:
250-round fabric belt (400rpm)

FN HIGH POWER

SPECIFICATIONS

FN HIGH POWER

Type:
  semi-automatic pistol

Calibre:
  9mm (0.354in) Parabellum

Length:
  0.197m (7.75in)

Length of barrel:
  0.118m (4.65in)

Weight:
  1.01kg (2.44lb) loaded

Muzzle velocity:
  351m (1150ft) per second

Feed:
  13-round detachable box magazine

A design dating from 1925, the FN (Browning) modèle GP or GP35 was the last pistol created by John Browning before his death and remains one of the best pistols ever produced. The High-Power design owed little to earlier Browning pistols and incorporated a positive breech lock.

The construction was very sturdy, and an unusual feature was the 13-round magazine, which resulted in a bulky but still easily holdable butt. FN's licensed production began in 1935, and the pistol was produced for the Belgian, Dutch, Danish, Lithuanian and Romanian forces. Just before Belgium's fall to Germany in May 1940, the drawings were taken to the UK and then transferred to the John Inglis Company of Toronto, Canada, where further production followed for China and then Canada and the UK. The Canadian model was slightly different from the Belgian pistol, and had no provision for the fitting of a wooden holster stock to the butt. In British and Canadian service the GP35 was the Pistol, Browning, FN, 9mm HP No. 1 Mks 1 and 1*, and No 2 Mks 1 and 1*. Further manufacture in Belgium under German control resulted in a pistol known as the 9mm Pistole 640(b). Amazingly, or perhaps not given its excellent design and build, this weapon is still in service around the world.

FN 1924

Belgium's main constructor of small arms, the *Fabrique Nationale d'Armes de Guerre* located in Herstal, licence-manufactured Mauser bolt-action rifles from 1889 for the Belgian Army and also for export. From 1919, the year after Germany's defeat in World War I, FN built an updated and shortened version of the definitive Mauser Gewehr 1898 rifle as the Fusil Mauser FN, modèle 1924, which provided FN with one of its greatest export successes. The modèle 1924 was so closely similar to the Karabiner 98k that after Belgium's 1940 defeat by Germany the FN production facility needed only very modest changes to produce this later German rifle. The modèle 1924 was initially offered in 7, 7.65 and 7.9mm calibres. Together with the only marginally different modèles 1924/30 and 1930, the modèle 1924 was sold to many countries including, amongst World War II's combatants, Brazil, China, Greece, Lithuania, Luxembourg and Yugoslavia. The last established its own production facility to manufacture the modèle 24 as the Puska 7.9mm M 24, which paved the way for two slightly shortened variants, the Sokol-Puska 7.9mm and the Komitern Puska 7.9mm. Belgium did not adopt the modèle 24 until 1939, and the few such weapons captured by the Germans were designated Gewehr 220(b) with a prefix indicating the calibre.

SPECIFICATIONS

FN 1924

Type:
  bolt-action rifle

Calibre:
  7, 7.65 and 7.92mm (0.276, 0.301 and 0.312in)

Length:
  1.10m (43in)

Length of barrel:
  0.589m (23.2in)

Weight:
  3.85kg (8.5lb) without bayonet

Muzzle velocity:
  750m (2461ft) per second with 7.5mm ammunition

Feed:
  5-round box magazine

ROSS RIFLE MK III

SPECIFICATIONS

ROSS RIFLE MK III

Type:
  bolt-action rifle

Calibre:
  7.7mm (0.303in)

Length:
  1.285m (50.56in)

Length of barrel:
  0.775m (30.15in)

Weight:
  4.48kg (9.75lb)

Muzzle velocity:
  792m (2600ft) per second

Feed:
  5-round box magazine

The first Ross rifle was manufactured in 1896, and in the period up to 1915 there were many development and service models. The primary model in service after 1914 was the Model 1910, known to the British Army as the Rifle, Magazine, Ross, Mk IIIB, and to the Canadians as the Rifle, Ross, Mk III. From 1916 – when the Short Magazine Lee Enfield was adopted in its place after the Canadian weapon had been shown by experience in the trench warfare of World War I to lack adequate strength and reliability – the Ross rifle was relegated from standard infantry frontline use, although it was still used with considerable success as a sniping rifle, often fitted with a telescopic sight.

In the period between the world wars examples of the Ross rifle were exported to Lithuania, and then passed into Soviet hands after the USSR's 1939 seizure of the Baltic states. During 1940 some 70,000 Ross rifles were sold to the UK by the USA, which had bought an initial 20,000 such rifles in 1917 for training in the USA. The majority of these rifles was allocated to the Home Guard, but some weapons were released to fishing boat and small merchant ship crews to provide a very limited anti-aircraft defence capability. A few Ross rifles were issued to second-line units of the British Army at a time when Britain was desperate for weapons.

ZK VZ.383

Otherwise known as the ZK 383, the ZK vz.383 was a Czechoslovakian submachine gun, which was designed in 1933 at Brno by Josef and Frantisek Koucky, and entered production in the same factory shortly after that time. The weapon was retained in manufacture right through to 1948, three years after the end of World War II. The reason for this was that the ZK vz.383 was a notably well designed and capably manufactured weapon. The gun was distinguished by a number of unusual features, these including a 0.17kg (0.375lb) weight that could be added to the bolt to slow the rate of fire, a folding bipod (discarded on the ZK vz.383P model for paramilitary service) under the barrel and, on the post-war ZK vz.383H model, a folding magazine.

Another feature that enhanced the capabilities of the ZK vz.383 was a quick-change mechanism for the barrel. The Czechoslovak Army adopted the ZK vz.383 as its standard sub-machine gun in 1933, and weapons of this useful type were also exported to Bulgaria as well as a number of South American countries, but after Germany's two-part seizure of Czechoslovakia in 1938 and 1939 the weapon remained in production to meet the requirements of the Waffen-SS. Most of the submachine guns manufactured in World War II bore the designation vz.9.

SPECIFICATIONS

ZK VZ.383

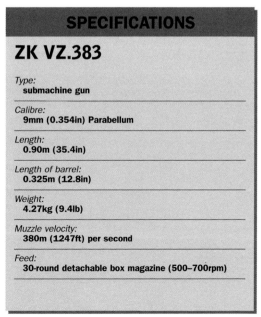

Type:
  submachine gun

Calibre:
  9mm (0.354in) Parabellum

Length:
  0.90m (35.4in)

Length of barrel:
  0.325m (12.8in)

Weight:
  4.27kg (9.4lb)

Muzzle velocity:
  380m (1247ft) per second

Feed:
  30-round detachable box magazine (500–700rpm)

ZB VZ/26

SPECIFICATIONS

ZB VZ/26

Type:
light air-cooled machine gun

Calibre:
7.92mm (0.312in)

Length:
1.161m (45.75in)

Barrel length:
0.672m (23.7in)

Weight:
9.6kg (21.3lb)

Muzzle velocity:
760m (2493ft) per second

Feed:
20- or 30-round detachable box magazine (550rpm)

The *Ceskoslovenska Zbrojovka* company, located at Brno (Brunn) in Czechoslovakia, was created in 1922, soon after the country's emergence after the end of World War I as an independent state out of the wreckage of the Austro-Hungarian Empire, and its first product was the Praga Model 24 belt-fed light machine gun designed by Vaclav Holek. A magazine-fed model was introduced some two years later as the ZB vz/26. This was an excellently designed and sturdily manufactured gun of the gas-operated type, and soon proved itself popular as it was exported to several parts of the world. The Czechoslovak Army ordered the type as its standard light machine gun, and these weapons were impressed by Germany after its 1939 seizure of that part of Czechoslovakia still left after the Munich agreement of 1938. Many countries secured licensed manufacturing agreements for the vz/26. The ZB vz/27 differed from the vz/26 only in small details, and further development led to the ZB vz/30 and thence, via the interim ZB vz/33, the British Bren Gun. The main versions of the vz/26 were the Czechoslovak 7.92mm Kulomet vz/26 (le MG 26[t]), Soviet 7.92mm Rutschnoi pulemet obrazets 1926 (le MG 146/2[r]) and Yugoslav 7.92mm Puska-Mitralez 7.9mm M26 Brunn (le MG 146/1[j]). Other users were China, Japan, Lithuania, Romania, Spain, Sweden and Turkey.

MADSEN

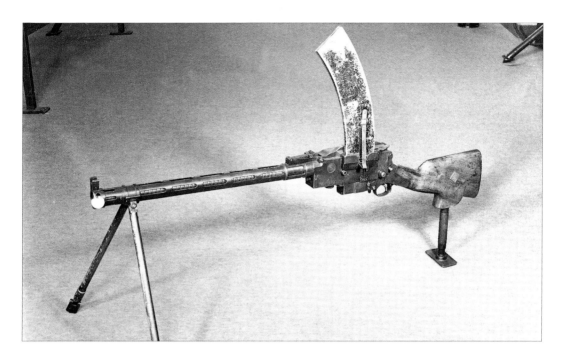

The first model of the Madsen light machine gun appeared during 1904, and the series then remained in production into the late 1950s in a large number of models and indeed calibres for export to many parts of the world. It is difficult to see why the Madsen light machine gun was a notable sales success as it was expensive and offered high capability in no particular respect, but the weapons were certainly well made and excellently engineered. Germany maintained production during its occupation of Denmark between 1940 and 1945. Many of the Dutch guns were seized by the Japanese during their conquest of the Dutch East Indies. The main variants used in World War II (with the German designation in parentheses where applicable) were the British 0.303in M1915, 1919, 1929, 1931 and 1939 (see specification); Bulgarian 8mm M1915, 1924 and 1927; Chinese 7.92mm M1916, 1930 and 1937; Danish 8mm Rekytgevaer M1903/24 (8mm le MG 158[d]), Rekytgevaer M1924 (8mm le MG 159[d]) and Rekytgevaer Madsen 8mm (s MG 258[d]); Dutch 6.5mm M1919, 1923, 1926, 1927, 1934, 1938 and 1939; Estonian 0.303in M1925 and 1937; Finnish 7.62mm M1910, 1920, 1921 and 1923; French 8mm M1915, 1919, 1922 and 1924 (8mm le MG 157[f]); German 7.92mm M1941 and 1942 (7.92mm MG [Madsen]); and Hungarian 7.92mm M1925 and 1943.

SPECIFICATIONS

MADSEN

Type:
light air-cooled machine gun

Calibre:
7.7mm (0.303in)

Length:
1.143m (45in)

Barrel length:
0.584m (23in)

Weight:
9.07kg (20lb)

Muzzle velocity:
715m (2346ft) per second

Feed:
20-, 25-, 30- and 40-round box magazines (450rpm)

KONEPISTOOLI M/31

SPECIFICATIONS

KONEPISTOOLI M/31

Type:
  submachine gun

Calibre:
  9mm (0.354in) Parabellum

Length:
  0.87m (34.25in)

Length of barrel:
  0.3175m (12.5in)

Weight:
  4.68kg (10.3lb)

Muzzle velocity:
  400m (1312ft) per second

Feed:
  20-, 50- and 71-round box or drum magazine (450rpm)

The family of Finnish submachine guns universally known as the "Suomi" was developed from 1922, resulting in the Koonepistooli m/26 as the first production model. This was chambered for the 7.63mm Mauser round, but in 1931 the m/31 was produced for the altogether superior 9mm Parabellum round. The m/1931 was one of the most far-reaching submachine gun designs ever created, and strongly influenced Soviet design thinking.

A capably designed and well-manufactured weapon, the m/31 was made under licence in Denmark, Sweden and Switzerland, as well as being produced in Finland for national use as well as export to countries such as Norway. By submachine gun standards the m/31 was both expensive and heavy as all of its major parts were machined from solid metal, but the weapon was notably accurate as a result of its long barrel. Madsen produced for Danish service the M42, which was later taken over by the Germans as the 9mm Maschinenpistole 746(d). The main problem with submachine guns in general was their accuracy and ammunition usage. In battle troops tended to fire bursts inaccurately, which, though it may have made them feel better, used a lot of ammunition for very little results. A division could use hundreds of thousands of rounds in a short space of time.

PISTOLE M1935

For reasons possibly of reliability but probably of tradition, the French Army was slow to consider and adopt the automatic pistol as a replacement for the revolver. When the service did opt for such a weapon, so unprepared for the switch was the French armaments industry that the service had initially to use a variety of Spanish weapons. Thus it was only in 1935 that the French Army fixed on its first automatic pistol of indigenous design by Charles Fetter of SACM, and this became the Pistole Automatique modèle 1935A.

The modèle 1935A was clearly derived from the Colt M1911A1 with modest changes in the recoil spring and locking mechanism as well as a different cartridge, the 7.65mm Long, only rarely used outside France. This fact severely hindered the possibility of export sales, and in fact the modèle 1935A was used only by France. The modèle 1935A was complemented by its modèle 1935S subvariant optimized for easier manufacture. The modèle 1935S was characterized by a straighter butt, revisions to the locking mechanism, and a muzzle extending slightly from the slide. The modèles 1935A and 1935S (specification at right) were both in service at the time of France's June 1940 defeat by Germany, which subsequently adopted both weapons with the designation 7.65mm Pistole 625(f).

SPECIFICATIONS

PISTOLE M1935

Type:
semi-automatic piston

Calibre:
7.65mm (0.301in) Long

Length:
0.188m (7.4in)

Length of barrel:
0.104m (4.1in)

Weight:
0.79kg (1.75lb)

Muzzle velocity:
345m (1132ft) per second

Feed:
8-round box magazine

FUSIL M1916

SPECIFICATIONS

FUSIL M1916

Type:
  bolt-action rifle

Calibre:
  8mm (0.315in)

Length:
  1.306m (51.4in)

Length of barrel:
  0.797m (31.4in)

Weight:
  4.2kg (9.25lb)

Muzzle velocity:
  725m (2379ft) per second

Feed:
  5-round fixed box magazine

By the middle of World War I the French Army had come to the belated recognition that the Mannlicher type of three-round fixed magazine (loaded with individual rounds) used by the Fusil modèle 07/15 was a severe tactical limitation, and therefore ordered the revision of this otherwise good weapon with a larger magazine loaded by means of a five-round charger. The resulting weapon was the Fusil d'Infanterie modèle 1916 (specifications in table left), which was most readily identifiable by the fact that the magazine now extended below the handguard.

After World War I large numbers of modèle 1916 rifles were delivered to many of France's European allies, most notably Greece, Poland, Romania and Yugoslavia, as well as ex-enemy Turkey. By 1939 only France and Yugoslavia were still using the weapon, and after Germany's 1940 and 1941 victories over these countries captured weapons were absorbed into the German inventory with the designations Gewehr 304(f) and, in the case of the Yugoslav Puska 8mm M16F, Gewehr 304(j). A carbine version of the Fusil modèle 1916 was also produced as the Mousqueton modèle 1916, upgraded in 1927 to modèle 16/27 standard. This weapon was exported to Romania and Yugoslavia, the latter using the type as the Karabini 8mm M16F.

FUSIL M07/1915

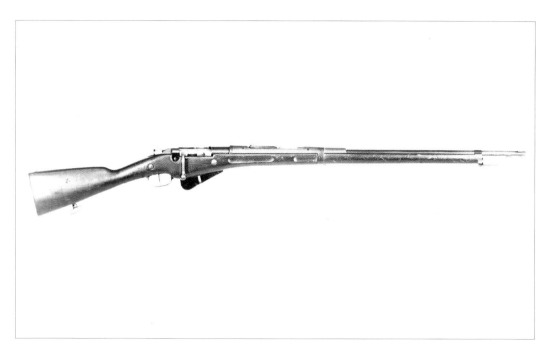

The designation Fusil d'Infanterie modèle 1907 transformé 1915 et modifié 1934 was the official name of the weapon that was a radical upgrade of the modèle 07/15, and was often called the Fusil modèle 1934 or Fusil modèle 07/15 M34.

This weapon was created in 1934 by shortening the modèle 07/15 and installing a new barrel to fire the 7.5mm Cartouche modèle 29 rimless round, which was now loaded into a five-round magazine of the Mauser pattern. The weapon that resulted from this process bore only a limited resemblance to the modèle 07/15 weapon, but despite being an altogether improved type, was not produced in large enough numbers to replace all the examples of the older rifle. Production of the modèle 07/15 M34 ended in 1940, by which time only part of the French Army had received the weapon. The total defeat at the hands of Nazi Germany in June 1940 naturally halted the army's weapons modernization programme.

The Germans, as with other weapons, took extant models into their own inventory with the designation Gewehr 241(f). It is worth noting that there was also a cavalry version of this rifle, and that this differed from the infantry weapon only in having a turned-down, rather than projecting-bolt, handle.

SPECIFICATIONS

FUSIL M07/1915

Type:
bolt-action rifle

Calibre:
7.5mm (0.295in)

Length:
1.084m (42.7in)

Length of barrel:
0.58m (22.8in)

Weight:
3.56kg (7.85lb)

Muzzle velocity:
825m (2707ft) per second

Feed:
5-round fixed box magazine

FUSIL MAS 36

SPECIFICATIONS

FUSIL MAS 36

Type:
  bolt-action rifle

Calibre:
  7.5mm (0.295in)

Length:
  1.019m (40.13in)

Length of barrel:
  0.574m (22.6in)

Weight:
  3.67kg (8.29lb)

Muzzle velocity:
  825m (2707ft) per second

Feed:
  5-round fixed box magazine

When the French Army switched from the 8mm Lebel rimmed to 7.5mm rimless cartridge in 1924 (Cartouche modèle 1924 later upgraded to Cartouche modèle 1929), it decided that the time was ripe for a new rifle created specifically to use the new cartridge. A prototype weapon appeared in 1932, but it was 1936 before the definitive Fusil MAS 36 was adopted. In many ways the MAS 36 could be regarded as an obsolescent weapon even at the time of its introduction, for by this time many armies were introducing or at least developing semi-automatic rifles. However, the French opted in the MAS 36 for bolt action, specifically of a modified Mauser type (with the locking lugs at the back of the receiver instead of the bolt head) and an awkward bolt handle angled forward and downwards. In common with other French rifles, the MAS 36 lacked any safety catch. The MAS 36 was the last bolt-action rifle adopted by a major power, and by 1939 and the outbreak of World War II full production was in hand at the *Manufacture d'Armes de Saint-Etienne*. After France's 1940 surrender, the Germans took over enough rifles to equip several of the divisions of its occupation force with what now became the Gewehr 242(f). Produced only in small numbers, the MAS 36 CR39 development of the MAS 36 for paratroops featured a folding aluminium butt.

HOTCHKISS M1909

Arguably the first genuine light machine gun to enter large-scale service anywhere in the world, the Fusil Mitrailleur Hotchkiss modèle 1909 was often called the "Benet-Mercier", and was based on features employed in the larger Hotchkiss machine guns, including the gas-operated mechanism and the feed by a metal strip that in the case of the modèle 1909 was inverted and often resulted in feed problems. During World War I the modèle 1909 was widely used by the French, and also delivered to the UK and USA. Improved Hotchkiss light machine guns were the modèle 1922 and heavy-barrel modèle 1926, both of which could have feed mechanisms other than the usual Hotchkiss strip. By the outbreak of World War II France and the USA had disposed of their weapons, but the UK kept limited numbers for airfield defence. Modèle 1909 weapons captured by the Germans included the British 0.303in Gun, Machine, Hotchkiss, Mks I and I* (7.7mm le MG 136[e] and le MG 136[g] taken from the British and Greeks), and modèles 1922 and 1926, including the French 6.5mm Fusil Mitrailleur Hotchkiss modèle 1922 (6.5mm le MG 105[f]) and 8mm Fusil Mitrailleur Hotchkiss modèle 1926 (8mm le MG 105[f]), Greek 6.5mm Hotchkiss Model 1926 (6.5mm le MG 104[g], 7.9mm Hotchkiss Model 1926 (7.9mm le MG 152/1[g]), and Hotchkiss Model 1926 (7.9mm le MG 152/2[g]).

SPECIFICATIONS

HOTCHKISS M1909

Type:
light air-cooled machine gun

Calibre:
7.92mm (0.312in)

Length:
1.22m (48in)

Length of barrel:
0.55m (21.65in)

Weight:
9kg (19.8lb)

Muzzle velocity:
745m (2444ft) per second

Feed:
25-round metal strip (500rpm)

HOTCHKISS M1914

SPECIFICATIONS

HOTCHKISS M1914

Type:
medium air-cooled machine gun

Calibre:
8mm (0.315in)

Length:
1.27m (50in)

Length of barrel:
0.775m (30.5in)

Weight:
23.6kg (52lb) excluding tripod

Muzzle velocity:
725m (2379ft) per second

Feed:
24- or 30-round strips, or 249-round belt (400–600rpm)

The first Hotchkiss machine guns entered French service in 1897, and from the next year the weapon was also exported. These modèles 1897 and 1898 were duly followed by the Mitrailleuse Hotchkiss modèles 1910 and 1914 weapons. All four were similar in their use of a gas-powered operating system, a heavy barrel with five large cooling rings, and the Hotchkiss metal strip feed arrangement. This last was a limiting feature because it limited burst lengths to a maximum of 40 rounds, so the modèle 1914 introduced a type of belt feed in which three-round "mini-strips" were connected into 249-round "belts". Well made and reliable, the Hotchkiss machine gun was produced in large numbers and, for the export market, in a variety of calibres. However, the Hotchkiss guns were heavy and bulky. Thus by 1939 most surviving weapons were used in the static role as defensive weapons. The Germans captured large numbers of weapons and placed them in German service: the Belgian 7.65mm Mitrailleuse "Hotchkiss" (7.65mm s MG 220[b]), French 8mm Mitrailleuse Hotchkiss modèle 1914 (8mm s MG 257[f]), Norwegian 6.5mm Hotchkiss mitralose m/98 (6.5mm s MG 201[n]) and Hotchkiss's 7.9mm mitralose m/98t (7.9mm s MG 240[n]), and Polish 7.9mm Karabin maszynowy Hotchkiss (14/25) (7.9mm s MG 238[p]).

HOTCHKISS M1930

During 1930 Hotchkiss introduced a larger-calibre version of its 11mm modèle de ballon anti-observation balloon machine gun of 1917 as the Mitrailleuse Hotchkiss de 13mm 2 modèle 1930. This looked like a scaled-up British Bren Gun and was fed by an 30-round overhead box magazine of curved shape, as dictated by the use of rimmed ammunition. The modèle 1930 was schemed for capability in a number of roles, with optimization in a given role provided by the gun's different mountings.

The three main variants were the Affût d'accompagnement à roues à une mitrailleuse Hotchkiss de 13mm 2 de cavalerie for infantry use on two spoked wheels and with a small limber for ammunition and spares, the Affût-trepied leger de cavalerie à une mitrailleuse Hotchkiss de 13mm 2 for cavalry use on a tripod, and the Affût-trepied R3 à deux mitrailleuses Hotchkiss de 13mm 2 for anti-aircraft use with two machine guns on a heavy tripod mounting with a complex sight. The modèle 1930 was exported in small numbers to Greece, Poland, Romania, the USSR and Yugoslavia, and was copied in Japan as the Type 93. Germany used captured French weapons with the designation 13.2mm MG 271(f). All in all, the Hotchkiss was an average weapon.

SPECIFICATIONS

HOTCHKISS M1930

Type:
heavy air-cooled machine gun

Calibre:
13.2mm (0.519in)

Length:
2.41m (95in)

Length of barrel:
1.65m (65in)

Weight:
37.5kg (87lb)

Muzzle velocity:
700m (2297ft) per second

Feed:
30-round box magazine (250–300rpm)

CHATELLERAULT

SPECIFICATIONS

CHATELLERAULT

Type:
light air-cooled machine gun

Calibre:
7.5mm (0.295in)

Length:
1.007m (39.65in)

Length of barrel:
0.50m (19.7in)

Weight:
8.93kg (19.7lb)

Muzzle velocity:
820m (2690ft) per second

Feed:
25-round detachable box magazine (450–600rpm)

Created as a light machine gun to supplant the unsatisfactory Chauchat in French service, the Fusil Mitrailleur Chatellerault modèle 1924 was a useful weapon based conceptually on an American weapon, the Browning Automatic Rifle, but with unusual features including two triggers: the front and rear triggers controlled single-shot and automatic fire respectively. The weapon and its specially designed round entered service before full development had been completed, however, and as a result there were a number of accidents including some caused by bursting barrels. Full development resulted in the modèle 1924/29, which was the French Army's standard light machine gun at the start of World War II.

The modèle 1924/29 was a first-rate weapon, and the Germans took captured examples into their own inventory with the designation 7.5mm le MG 116(f), while a few modèle 1924 weapons became 7.5mm le MG 115(f) guns. Developed from the modèle 1924/29 for use in fixed defences and armoured fighting vehicles, the Mitrailleuse de 7.5mm modèle 1931 had a butt of odd contours and was fed with ammunition from a 150-round drum magazine mounted on the left-hand side of the weapon. The Germans used this machine gun in the anti-aircraft role with the designation 7.5mm Kpfw MG 331(f).

PISTOLE 08

Generally known as the "Luger", the Pistole 08 is amongst the most celebrated pistols ever placed in production. The first Luger pistols for military service were manufactured in 1900 to meet a Swiss order, and the type was also adopted by the German navy during 1904 and then by the German Army in 1908. It was this last order that led to the designation P 08, which became the most important of some 35 or more Luger pistol variants. The P 08 was the standard German service pistol until 1938, when the P 38 was introduced as its successor, but even so the P 08 remained in production to 1943 and at the end of World War II in 1945 remained in full service for lack of adequate numbers of the P 38. Oddly enough, the P 08 was not a first-class weapon for military use as it was susceptible to jamming when its open toggle mechanism was clogged by dirt. On the other side of the coin, however, the P 08 was a very "pointable" weapon and was therefore fairly accurate. The most common P 08 version had a 0.103m (4.06in) barrel, but the barrel of the naval model was 0.152m (6in) long. Other than Germany, countries that used the P 08 included Abyssinia, Bulgaria, Finland, Latvia, the Netherlands, Persia, Portugal, Romania, Switzerland and Turkey: the Dutch weapons were produced in the UK by Vickers during the early 1920s.

SPECIFICATIONS

PISTOLE 08

Type:
semi-automatic pistol

Calibre:
9mm (0.354in) Parabellum

Length:
0.222m (8.75in)

Length of barrel:
0.103m (4.06in)

Weight:
0.876kg (1.93lb)

Muzzle velocity:
320m (1050ft) per second

Feed:
8-round detachable straight box magazine

WALTHER PP

SPECIFICATIONS

WALTHER PP

Type:
  semi-automatic pistol

Calibre:
  7.65 or 9mm (0.301 or 0.354in)

Length:
  0.162m (6.38in)

Length of barrel:
  0.085m (3.35in)

Weight:
  0.708kg (1.56lb)

Muzzle velocity:
  290m (951ft) per second with 7.65mm ammunition

Feed:
  8-round detachable straight box magazine

A semi-automatic pistol that was first delivered in 1929, the Walther Model PP had been designed for police use as indicated by its full designation, Polizei Pistole (police pistol). The pistol used the Walther double-action trigger mechanism that was also used on the later P 38, and other features included a lightweight receiver and, next to the hammer, a signal button that protruded when the weapon was loaded.

In overall terms the design was light and slim. From 1939 the Model PP was manufactured for military service in 7.65mm and 9mm calibres, the main operators being the German Air Force (Luftwaffe) and the German Army's tank (panzer) arm, both of which needed a small weapon. Introduced in 1931, the Model PPK was a smaller version of the Model PP and was initially manufactured for easy carriage by plain clothes policemen as indicated by the full designation, Polizei Pistole Kriminal (criminal police pistol).

Except for its smaller size, the Model PPK was similar to the Model PP and was delivered for service use (especially by the German Air Force) from 1939. The Model PPK was chambered for the same calibre as the Model PP, the magazine holding seven 7.65mm or six 9mm rounds. Like most German small arms, the PP was manufactured to a high standard.

WALTHER P38

The Pistole 38, another semi-automatic weapon from the Walther stable, entered service with the German armed forces in 1938 as successor to the P 08. It embodied a double-action trigger mechanism developed from the earlier Models PP and PPK, and also featured the signal pin which extended beside the hammer when there was a round in the chamber. The P 38 was mechanically reliable and in service was a popular weapon, being able to withstand extremes of temperature and inhospitable terrain (especially in the USSR), but was never produced in numbers large enough to allow complete replacement of the P 08. Manufacture was undertaken in Belgium and Bohemia-Moravia (occupied Czechoslovakia) as well as in Germany itself.

There were a number of production subvariants, each differing from the baseline model only in small details, before the P 38 was taken out of production in 1945, and although the weapon's manufacture became cruder as World War II progressed (a result of raw material shortages that affected the whole of the German armaments industry), the P 38 was always reliable. Indeed, so useful was the type that it was later placed back in production to meet the requirements of the army of the Federal German Republic.

SPECIFICATIONS

WALTHER P38

Type:
semi-automatic pistol

Calibre:
9mm (0.354in) Parabellum

Length:
0.2185m (8.6in)

Length of barrel:
0.1245m (4.9in)

Weight:
0.95kg (2.1lb)

Muzzle velocity:
340m (1115ft) per second

Feed:
8-round detachable straight box magazine

KARABINER 98K

SPECIFICATIONS

KARABINER 98K

Type:
  bolt-action rifle

Calibre:
  7.92mm (0.312in)

Length:
  1.1075m (43.6in)

Length of barrel:
  0.739m (23.6in)

Weight:
  3.9kg (8.6lb)

Muzzle velocity:
  755m (2477ft) per second

Feed:
  5-round fixed box magazine

In World War I the German Army decided that its standard rifle, the Gewehr 98, was too long for effective use. There was little that could be done at the time, but by 1924 Mauser had developed a rifle shorter than its Gewehr 98 and based on its "Standard" model for export sales: this was manufactured in Belgium and other countries, but did not enter German production until 1935 as the Karabiner 98k (the letter suffix standing for *kurz*, or short). German production resulted in the delivery of millions of these weapons before 1945, and numbers were further boosted by manufacture in Belgium and Bohemia-Moravia (occupied Czechoslovakia). As was inevitable in a programme of this size and duration, there were a number of variations in length, weight and furniture: late-production Kar 98k weapons, for instance, lacked any bayonet lug. Service experience confirmed that the Kar 98k was both sturdy and accurate, but also that the small capacity of the five-round magazine was a tactical disadvantage. Another rifle based on the "Standard" Mauser rifle was the 7.92mm Model Chiang Kai-shek, or "Generalissimo", that was introduced in 1935 and was to all intents and purposes identical to the Kar 98k. Another close relative of the Kar 98k was the Belgian 7.65mm Fusil modèle 35 that was later taken into German service as the Gewehr 262(b).

GEWEHR 41

In 1940 the Germany Army, currently equipped with bolt-action weapons so far as rifles and carbines were concerned, issued a requirement for a semi-automatic (or self-loading) rifle to succeeded the various Mauser weapons of the Gewehr 98 series. The requirement elicited very similar designs from Mauser and Walther, and the German authorities ordered prototypes of each type for competitive evaluation before any major production contracts were placed. Mauser's Gewehr 41(M) rapidly revealed itself to be inadequate for service, while Walther's Gewehr 41(W) (see specifications) received the order. The Gew 41(W) was based on virtually the same gas-operated mechanism as the Gew 41(M), namely a variant of a Danish system. This Bang system trapped muzzle gases and diverted them rearward to power a piston that operated the ejection/loading mechanism. As well as being difficult to produce, the Gew 41(W) was not an operational success for it was difficult to load quickly and its complicated mechanism led to an unacceptably low level of reliability. Other limitations were the weapon's considerable weight and also a design that made the weapon unhandy. Production was terminated after the advent of the Gewehr 43, but the type remained in service to the end of World War II, being used mainly on the Eastern Front.

SPECIFICATIONS

GEWEHR 41

Type:
semi-automatic rifle

Calibre:
7.92mm (0.312in)

Length:
1.175m (46.25in)

Length of barrel:
0.5525m (21.75in)

Weight:
5.1kg (11.25lb)

Muzzle velocity:
775m (2543ft) per second

Feed:
10-round fixed straight box magazine

GEWEHR 43

SPECIFICATIONS

GEWEHR 43

Type:
  semi-automatic rifle

Calibre:
  7.92mm (0.312in)

Length:
  1.117m (44in)

Length of barrel:
  0.55m (21.6in)

Weight:
  4.4kg (9.56lb)

Muzzle velocity:
  775m (2543ft) per second

Feed:
  10-round detachable straight box magazine

When they evaluated the Tokarev semi-automatic rifle, of which they captured numerous examples in 1941 and 1942, the Germans quickly appreciated that the Soviet gas-operated system offered several advantages over the modified Bang system used in their Gewehr 41 weapons. It was seen that the Russian gas-operated mechanism had many advantages over the system used on the Gew 41. The Gew 41(W) was already in production, but the Germans now modified the action to a system modelled closely on that of the Soviet self-loading rifle to create the Gewehr 43 firing the German Army's standard 7.92mm cartridge. Initial tests confirmed that the Gew 43 was an altogether better weapon than the Gew 41(W), offering much greater reliability under all operating conditions, and the new type replaced the Gew 41(W) in production. The new self-loading rifle was simpler, and therefore quicker and cheaper, to manufacture, and the opportunity was taken to introduce features such as a reduction in machined components, an increase in forged parts, laminated rather than solid wooden furniture, and a detachable magazine that could be loaded with two standard five-round clips. The weapon was completed with provision for the Zf41 telescopic sight as standard, and from 1944 there was also a Karabiner 43 version shortened by some 50mm (1.97in).

FG 42

The German paratroop arm was an element of the air force, and many of its weapons were therefore different from those of the army. Thus when the army issued its specification for an assault rifle, the air force decided not to adopt the 7.92mm *kurz* (short) intermediate-power round and therefore contracted with Rheinmetall-Borsig for an assault rifle suitable for airborne use and chambered for the original 7.92mm high-power round. The resulting Fallschirmjägergewehr 42 was one of the most remarkable weapons developed in World War II, for although there was nothing entirely novel, the FG 42 marked an evolutionary stage in the development of the compact assault rifle with a straight-through design. In some respects the FG 42 had affinities to the light machine gun, especially in features such as the permanently attached bipod that could be fixed at any point on the exposed barrel. Other notable elements of the design were the muzzle brake/compensator and the fixed folding bayonet, but a poor aspect was the lack of any provision for the barrel to be changed easily. The FG 42 was delivered in two main variants, one with a steel butt and a sloping pistol grip, and the other with a wooden butt and conventional grip. The weapon was expensive to manufacture, and as a result only 7000 were completed.

SPECIFICATIONS

FG 42

Type:
airborne forces assault rifle

Calibre:
7.92mm (0.312in)

Length:
0.94m (37in)

Length of barrel:
0.502m (19.75in)

Weight:
4.53kg (9.94lb)

Muzzle velocity:
760m (2493ft) per second

Feed:
20-round magazine (750–800rpm)

STURMGEWEHR 44

SPECIFICATIONS

STURMGEWEHR 44

Type:
assault rifle

Calibre:
7.92mm (0.312in)

Length:
0.94m (37in)

Length of barrel:
0.419m (16.5in)

Weight:
5.22kg (11.5lb)

Muzzle velocity:
650m (2,133ft) per second

Feed:
30-round detachable box magazine (500rpm)

Experience with the 8000 examples of the Haenel Maschinenkarabiner 42(H) assault rifle used for operational trials on the Eastern Front was generally successful, but indicated the need for changes whose implementation created the Maschinenpistole 43 firing the same 7.92mm *kurz* (short) intermediate-power round. The first MP 43s were delivered in 1943, and the type was retained in manufacture without noticeable change, except to facilitate production, right to the end of World War II. The MP 43/1 appeared late in 1943 and differed from the MP 43 only in its provision for the installation of a grenade-launcher cup at the muzzle. In 1944 the designation was changed to MP 44 for no apparent reason, although some MP 44 weapons had provision for a telescopic sight, and the definitive designation adopted late in 1944 was Sturmgewehr 44 or StG 44, an appellation selected for political rather than military reasons. The weapons of the MP 43 family were very effective, and may in fact be regarded as the first truly successful assault rifles that in many ways paved the way for assault rifle development after World War II. Among the accessories for the series were the Zielgerät 1229 "Vampir" infra-red night sight that appeared in small numbers during 1945, and the Krummlauf (curved leaf) barrel fitting and sight allowing the weapon to be fired round an angle of 30°.

MP 28/II

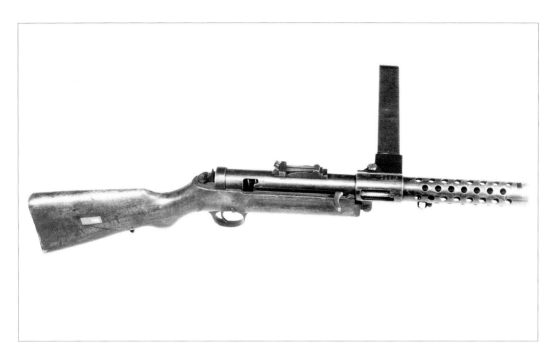

The Maschinenpistole 28/II sub-machine was in essence a 1928 development of the MP 18/I, which entered service in 1918 as the German Army's first such weapon, by Hugo Schmeisser for production by Haenel (interestingly, his name would be internationally associated with the later MP 38 and 40, though in fact he had very little to do with these weapons – the association is largely the result of Hollywood fantasy). The MP 28/II had a fire selector (single-shot or automatic) rather than the MP 18/I's automatic fire only, and less evident were a number of internal modifications. The type was produced as a commercial venture aimed at the export market, and was therefore produced in a number of calibres with particular features to suit the weapon to its various buyers. The weapon sold well to countries in South America, as well as to Belgium, China and Japan. The type was also made in Spain and Belgium (*Etablissements Anciens Pieper* at Herstal) as the Belgian Army's Mitraillette 34, and indeed many MP 28/II models were licence-made at Herstal for export. The MP 28/II saw extensive service in the Spanish Civil War, and after the outbreak of World War II in September 1939 all German production went to the German armed forces, which also used captured Belgian weapons after 1940 with the official designation MP 740(b).

SPECIFICATIONS

MP 28/II

Type:
submachine gun

Calibre:
9mm (0.354mm) Parabellum

Length:
0.81m (32in)

Length of barrel:
0.20m (7.9in)

Weight:
4kg (8.8lb)

Muzzle velocity:
380m (1247ft) per second

Feed:
20-, 32- 50-round detachable magazine (500rpm)

ERMA

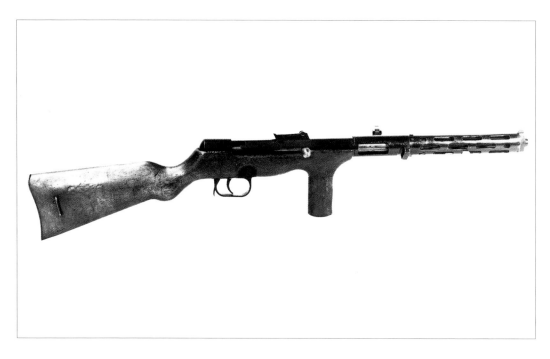

SPECIFICATIONS

ERMA

Type:
submachine gun

Calibre:
9mm (0.354in) Parabellum

Length:
0.90m (35.5in)

Length of barrel:
0.25m (9.9in)

Weight:
4.15kg (9.2lb)

Muzzle velocity:
380m (1247ft) per second

Feed:
20- or 32-round detachable box magazine (500rpm)

The Maschinenpistole Erma (or MPE) was designed in the early 1930s by Heinrich Vollmer for the Erfurter Maschinenfabrik company, hence the weapon's name. The Erma was a development of a Vollmer design of the mid-1920s, which featured a main spring enclosed in a telescopic tube to keep out dirt and other matter that might otherwise have jammed the action: this system became standard in subsequent German submachine guns such as the MP 38 and MP 40. Other features of the MPE were the extensive use of steel tube to reduce manufacturing time and cost, and the vertical wooden fore grip, although some of the weapons had a horizontal fore grip. The MPE appeared in time to be adopted for the German Army at the time of its initial expansion after the rise to power of the Nazi party in 1933, and remained a first-line German weapon until 1942, when surviving MPE submachine guns were relegated to second-line use. Modest numbers of MPE submachine guns were delivered to France for service with the official designation Pistolet Mitrailleur Vollmer Erma, and Yugoslavia also took the type in a variant with a lengthened barrel. The MPE was also manufactured in Spain and saw use in the Spanish Civil War. A subvariant manufactured in small quantities was a silenced model for the security police of the Vichy French regime operating under German supervision.

MP 38

The Maschinenpistole 38 is one of the most celebrated, or perhaps infamous, submachine guns ever placed in service. Designed by the Erma-Werke, the MP 38 introduced a number of unusual and innovative features: the main spring was contained within a telescopic sleeve (as pioneered in the limited-production MP Erma), the butt could be folded, and there was no wood in the weapon, which was therefore entirely of steel and plastic construction. Created from the outset for service with airborne and motorized troops (and thus with the folding butt), the MP 38 had a magazine located vertically under the weapon.

The MP 38 entered production in 1938 and was succeeded in 1940 by the MP 40. Combat experience with the MP 38 in Poland during September 1939 revealed the need for a safety mechanism on the cocking handle when this was in the forward (round cambered) position, when a knock could result in the weapon firing: thus a folding latch was added on the cocking handle to engage a notch on the receiver when forward, thus preventing any movement of the bolt. This created the MP38/40, and the feature was gradually added to most surviving MP 38 weapons after 1940. Contrary to popular belief, Hugo Schmeisser was never involved in the design of the weapon.

SPECIFICATIONS

MP 38

Type:
submachine gun

Calibre:
9mm (0.354in) Parabellum

Length:
0.833m (32.8in), butt extended

Length of barrel:
0.252m (9.9in)

Weight:
4.086kg (9lb)

Muzzle velocity:
380m (1247ft) per second

Feed:
32-round detachable box magazine (500rpm)

MP 40

SPECIFICATIONS

MP 40

Type:
submachine gun

Calibre:
9mm (0.354in) Parabellum

Length:
0.833m (32.8in), butt extended

Length of barrel:
0.252m (9.9in)

Weight:
4.027kg (8.88lb)

Muzzle velocity:
380m (1247ft) per second

Feed:
32-round detachable box magazine (500rpm)

The MP 38 was a technical and tactical success, but was also expensive to manufacture in terms of materials and time. The MP 38 was therefore re-designed as the Maschinenpistole 40 that was generally similar to the MP 38 but far easier to manufacture, as machining was reduced to a minimum and the use of welding and pressed components was maximized. As well as speeding production, these changes also made it possible for the MP 40 to be made by a larger number of companies drawing on the efforts of a pool of subcontractors delivering subassemblies. The MP 40 thus inaugurated the era of the swift and cheap manufacture of basic small arms, and was one of the most important submachine guns of World War II. Operational use of the weapon on the Eastern Front revealed that the MP 40 was not without its limitations, however, most notably by comparison with the Soviets' PPSh submachine gun that could be fitted with a 71-round drum magazine. This led to the creation of the MP 40/II that introduced a wider magazine housing to carry a side-by-side pair of MP 40 magazines: when the first magazine had been emptied, the complete assembly could be pushed over to bring the second magazine into position. The MP 40/II was delivered from 1943, but was not notably effective and was therefore manufactured only in modest numbers.

MP 41

Given the fact that far-sighted submachine guns such as the MP 38 and MP 40, with their all-metal construction and features to facilitate mass production, had clearly indicated the most practical line of development for such weapons under wartime conditions, the Maschinenpistole 41 could be seen only as something of an anachronism demanding somewhat greater manufacturing resources for a weapon that offered little operational advantage, something that Germany really could not afford given the industrial power of the enemies ranged against her.

The weapon was manufactured by Haenel on the basis of a development, by Hugo Schmeisser, of the MP 40. The MP 41 retained the barrel, bolt and operating mechanism of the MP 40 in combination with wooden furniture (including a full stock) derived conceptually from that of MP 28/II.

Neither the German armed forces not the police ordered the weapon, so it is uncertain why the type in fact entered production. As it was, only very small numbers of this weapon were completed, possibly for delivery to the forces of a country allied to Germany. Whatever the reason, the MP 41 submachine gun seems to have been a complete waste of time, manpower and precious German resources.

SPECIFICATIONS

MP 41

Type:
submachine gun

Calibre:
9mm (0.354in) Parabellum

Length:
0.865m (34in)

Length of barrel:
0.25m (9.9in)

Weight:
3.7kg (8.15lb)

Muzzle velocity:
380m (1247ft) per second

Feed:
32-round detachable magazine (500rpm)

MG 08

SPECIFICATIONS

MG 08

Type:
heavy water-cooled machine gun

Calibre:
7.92mm (0.312in)

Length:
1.175m (46.25in)

Length of barrel:
0.719m (28.3in)

Weight:
62kg (136.7lb) with spares

Muzzle velocity:
900m (2953ft) per second

Feed:
250-round fabric belt (300–450rpm)

The Schwere Maschinengewehr 08 (specification at left) was one of Germany's most important weapons of World War I, and numbers remained in service up to the outbreak of World War II as there were insufficient MG 34 weapons to replace them. By 1942 the s MG 08 had been retired to second-line duties. Captured weapons used by the Germans (with their new designations) included the Belgian 7.65mm Mitrailleuse "Maxim" (7.65mm s MG 221[b]), Lithuanian 7.92mm (7.9mm s MG 248[r]), Polish 7.92mm Maxsim 08 (7.9mm s MG 248[r]) and Yugoslav 7.92mm Mitralez 7.9mm M8M (7.9mm s MG 248[j]). The leichte MG 08/15 was a lightened version of the s MG 08 that kept its predecessor's mechanism and water-cooling, but was fitted with a bipod rather than being installed on a heavy tripod, and had a pistol grip and shoulder stock in place of the s MG 08's pair of spade grips. Turning the scales at a hefty 18kg (39.7lb), the le MG 08/15 was still in first-line service in 1939 but had been retired to second-line use by 1941. Captured weapons used by the Germans included the Belgian 7.65mm Mitrailleuse "Maxim" légère (7.65mm le MG 125[b]), Soviet 7.9mm Rutschnoi pulemet "Maksima" obrazets 08/15 (7.9mm le MG 145[r]), and Yugoslav 7.9mm Leki-Mitralez M8/15M (7.9mm le MG 145[j]).

MG 34

The Maschinengewehr 34 was designed by engineers at the Mauser factory at Obendorff, and major features of this superb machine gun included a quick-change barrel, connection of major components by bayonet catches, high-impact plastic stock, combined recoil booster and flash hider, straight-through design, and a system in which pressure on the upper and lower parts of the trigger produced semi-automatic and automatic fire respectively. In overall terms, therefore, the MG 34 was not so much a light/medium machine gun as the world's first general-purpose machine gun. In the light role the MG 34 was fired off a light bipod, with the Dreifuss 34 tripod mounting used for the anti-aircraft role. In the heavy machine gun role the MG 34 was installed on the Lafette 34 tripod mounting that could also be adapted for the anti-aircraft task. Several other mountings were available to suit the weapon to service in armoured fighting vehicles, wheeled vehicles and fixed fortification, while there were also twin and triple mountings for extra capability in the anti-aircraft task. The MG 34 entered service in 1936 and remained in production and service until 1945. It was an excellent gun, and was especially notable for its accuracy and high rate of fire. The MG 34's one major "failing" was its expense in terms of manufacturing cost and time.

SPECIFICATIONS

MG 34

Type:
general-purpose air-cooled machine gun

Calibre:
7.92mm (0.312in)

Length:
1.219m (48in)

Length of barrel:
0.627m (24.75in)

Weight:
11.5kg (26.7lb) with bipod

Muzzle velocity:
755m (2477ft) per second

Feed:
50-round belt, 50- or 75-round magazine (900rpm)

MG 42

SPECIFICATIONS

MG 42

Type:
general-purpose air-cooled machine gun

Calibre:
7.92mm (0.312in)

Length:
1.22m (48in)

Length of barrel:
0.533m (21in)

Weight:
11.5kg (25lb) with bipod

Muzzle velocity:
755m (2477ft) per second

Feed:
50-round belt, 50- or 75-round magazine (1500rpm)

Without doubt one of the most far-sighted and influential machine guns created in World War II, the Maschinengewehr 42 was in terms of its design and manufacturing requirements a truly outstanding weapon that has exercised a long-lasting influence over later general-purpose machine guns. The Mauser-designed MG 42 began life as the MG 39/41, whose origins could be found in the MG 34 and some Polish thinking. Like the MG 34, the MG 34 could be installed on several alternative mountings, but so far as troops in the field were concerned the MG 42's primary advantage over the MG 34 was its higher rate of fire. The locking system was novel but simple and reliable, the barrel-change system was quick and easy (as demanded by the high rate of fire), and the greatest innovation was the ease with which the weapon could be produced: the use of stampings and spot welding wherever possible to reduce cost and hasten production even when only semi-skilled labour was available. The MG 42 first saw service in North Africa during 1942, and from that time onward the weapon became one of Germany's most important and feared tactical weapons. A final development was the MG 45 with a different mechanism and an even higher rate of fire, but this was only just entering service as the war ended.

REVOLVER NO 2 MK I

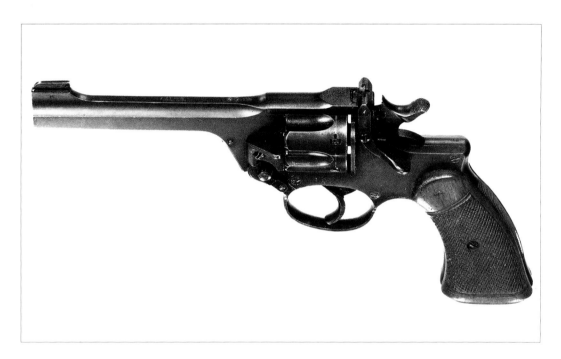

During World War I the British found that while their 0.455in pistol round offered excellent combat capability, the No 1 revolver from which it was fired was too heavy and cumbersome for battlefield use (though the weapon was very accurate). What was needed, the British decided, was a smaller round fired from a lighter pistol that could be handled more easily by men lacking extensive training in the use of heavy pistols. This resulted in the selection of the 0.38in round, for which Webley & Scott created a new pistol that was modified by the Royal Small Arms Factory at Enfield to enter service in 1932 as the Pistol, Revolver, No 2 Mk I. This was a very substantial and well made weapon, but was not deemed wholly satisfactory and was supplanted from 1938 by the No 2 Mk I* pistol with a lighter trigger pull, changed grips and provision for double-action use (requiring the removal of the thumb catch on the hammer).

The No 2 Mk I* was a reliable weapon but was not useful except at close range as the double action made accurate aiming very difficult. From July 1942 the No 2 Mk I** was introduced as a more easily produced model, and one of the changes was the hammer safety stop. The one great advantage with the weapon was its robustness, which meant it could be used in any theatre.

SPECIFICATIONS

REVOLVER NO 2 MK I

Type:
revolver pistol

Calibre:
9.65mm (0.38in)

Length:
0.26m (10.25in)

Length of barrel:
0.127m (5in)

Weight:
0.766kg (1.68lb)

Muzzle velocity:
183m (600ft) per second

Feed:
6-round revolving cylinder

REVOLVER NO 1 MK VI

SPECIFICATIONS

REVOLVER NO 1 MK VI

Type:
  revolver pistol

Calibre:
  11.56mm (0.455in)

Length:
  0.29m (11.25in)

Length of barrel:
  0.15m (6in)

Weight:
  1.09kg (2.4lb)

Muzzle velocity:
  189m (620ft) per second

Feed:
  6-round revolving cylinder

The huge 0.455in Webley revolver entered service with the British Army in 1887 after design as a powerful "man stopper" for use mainly in colonial warfare (the British had several disconcerting experiences during their colonial wars, during which native enemies displayed an alarming habit of not dropping to the ground when hit by a round). The final version of this series was introduced in 1915 and became the Pistol, Revolver, .455 No 1 Mk VI.

The other side of the weapon's capability as a potent man-stopper was its weight and general unhandiness, which made it difficult to aim and fire the weapon instinctively at anything but point-blank range. Effective employment of the pistol required considerable training and practice of the types not readily possible in World War I, and this led to the decision to adopt a smaller-calibre revolver, the 9.65mm (0.38in) No 2 weapon. However, at the start of World War II in September 1939 there were large numbers of the 0.455in revolver still in service, and in the UK the type equipped regular units as well as the Home Guard. The Germans felt that the weapon was still useful, for they issued captured revolvers of this type to second-line unit for service with the revised designation Revolver 665(e). As with all Webleys, the design was well made and robust.

RIFLE NO 3 MK I

Teething problems with the Rifle No 1, introduced in 1907, led to consideration of a replacement type firing a 7mm (0.276in) round. The P.13 development model of 1913 was based on a modified Mauser bolt action, but further work of the P.14 definitive model was postponed until 1915, when a variant in 7.7mm (0.303 in) calibre was ordered from American manufacturers for service as the Rifle No 3 Mk I (see specification). The USA later adopted a variant in 7.62mm (0.3in) calibre as the Rifle M1917. The P.14 was long and as a consequence somewhat difficult to handle, but was very accurate and therefore used mainly for sniping. From 1919 the surviving rifles were placed in store, and in 1940 the USA sold more than 750,000 M1917 weapons to the UK, mostly for service with the Home Guard. In 1940, British-made No 3 rifles were converted for sniper use with the designation No 3 Mk I(T), and this saw limited service up to 1943. A variant was the No 3 Mk I(T)A with an Aldis sight. During the interwar period Belgium bought numbers of No 3 rifles, possibly weapons that had been provided to Belgian troops in World War I. FN rebored these guns to 7.92mm calibre, and weapons of this type seized by the Germans after their May 1940 conquest of Belgium were taken into service with the designation Gewehr 284(b).

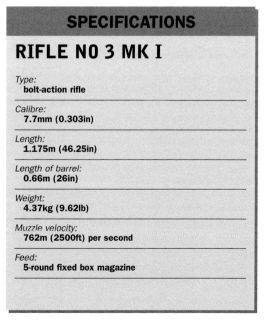

SPECIFICATIONS

RIFLE NO 3 MK I

Type:
bolt-action rifle

Calibre:
7.7mm (0.303in)

Length:
1.175m (46.25in)

Length of barrel:
0.66m (26in)

Weight:
4.37kg (9.62lb)

Muzzle velocity:
762m (2500ft) per second

Feed:
5-round fixed box magazine

RIFLE NO 4 MK I

SPECIFICATIONS

RIFLE NO 4 MK I

Type:
bolt-action rifle

Calibre:
7.7mm (0.303in)

Length:
1.129m (44.43in)

Length of barrel:
0.64m (25.2in)

Weight:
4.14kg (9.125lb)

Muzzle velocity:
751m (2465ft) per second

Magazine:
10-round detachable box magazine

Work on the design of a rifle to succeed No 1 Mk III* weapon started during 1924. The initial result was the No 1 Mk VI that reached the trials stage and formed the basis of a generally similar rifle optimized for mass production using modern manufacturing techniques. The new weapon was the Rifle No 4 Mk I that first appeared in 1931, although the UK's straitened financial circumstances of the period meant that full-scale manufacture did not start until 1940.

Although a primary consideration in its design had been ease of production, the No 4 Mk I was in no way an indifferent weapon as it was more accurate than earlier models as a result of its heavier barrel and longer sight base. However, the rifle was rushed into production during 1940 and this led to the emergence of several teething problems when the new weapon entered full-scale service in the following year.

A revision of assembly practices cured these difficulties, and the No 4 rifle then streamed off the production lines in vast numbers. The No 4 Mk I*, with only slight differences, was placed in production in Canada and the USA, and the weapon was also made in India. Another variant, the No 4 Mk I(T), was a sniping model with a telescopic sight and a cheek stock. This rifle was a very robust weapon.

STEN GUN

One of the weapons which the British Army needed most urgently as it sought to re-equip after its expulsion from mainland Europe in June 1940 was a submachine gun that was cheap and easy to manufacture. At the Royal Small Arms Factory at Enfield Lock R.V. Shepperd and H.J. Turpin created a very simple weapon that was accepted as the Sten.

Cheapness and ease of manufacture drove the basic design, and the Sten Mk I entered service in the summer of 1941. The Mk I had a flash hider and a wooden fore-stock and grip, but the Mk I* lacked these. Then came the Mk II (the specifications for which are given in the table at right) that was an even simpler weapon: the barrel, for example, was a drawn steel tube with only two rifling grooves, although these were later increased in number to six. Fairly reliable and very simple to maintain, the Sten was also easy to conceal and was much favoured by resistance forces. Germany used captured weapons with the designation Maschinenpistole 749(e) and produced copies as the MP 3008. The Mk II(S) was also a silenced version of the Mk II, the Mk III was a simplified version of the Mk I, the Mk IV was an experimental model for airborne forces, the Mk V was a less austere version of the Mk III, and the Mk VI was a silenced Mk V.

SPECIFICATIONS

STEN GUN

Type:
submachine gun

Calibre:
9mm (0.354in) Parabellum

Length:
0.762m (30in)

Length of barrel:
0.197m (7.75in)

Weight:
3kg (6.625lb)

Muzzle velocity:
366m (1200ft) per second

Feed:
32-round detachable box magazine (540rpm)

BREN GUN

SPECIFICATIONS

BREN GUN

Type:
light air-cooled machine gun

Calibre:
7.7mm (0.303in)

Length:
1.155m (45.5in)

Length of barrel:
0.635m (25in)

Weight:
9.95kg (22.12lb)

Muzzle velocity:
744m (2440ft) per second

Feed:
30-round detachable curved box magazine (500rpm)

The Bren Gun, one of the most famous light machine guns of World War II, had its origins in a Czechoslovak weapon, the ZB vz/26, via the vz/27, vz/30, vz/33 and vz/34. This superb gas-operated light machine gun entered production during 1937, its name reflecting its design origins in Brno and manufacture at Enfield Lock. There were four main models in World War II. The Mk I (specification at left) featured an adjustable bipod, butt handle and a rear sight of the radial type, gradually replaced in the Mk II by simpler and cheaper elements as wartime exigencies started to bite. The closely related Mks III and IV were both introduced in 1944 with a shorter and lighter barrel and, in the case of the Mk IV, changes to the butt.

The Bren Gun was at first made only at Enfield Lock, but production then spread to Australia, Canada and India. The Bren Gun was widely used by resistance forces in Europe, a task in which the weapon's light weight, accuracy, good firepower, reliability and ease of maintenance were invaluable. The Germans used captured weapons with the designation 7.7mm leichte Maschinengewehr 138(e). In British use the weapon was mounted on many different types of vehicle mounting and several tripod mountings were developed to complement the standard bipod.

VICKERS-BERTHIER

During 1925 Vickers obtained rights to the Berthier light machine gun, beginning manufacture of the Vickers-Berthier with weapons for export and British trials. The British Army preferred the Bren Gun, but the Indian Army secured large numbers for use as its standard light machine gun. The Mks I and II came from the UK, but then Indian production produced the Mks III (specification at right) and IIIB. The Vickers-Berthier light machine gun was reliable, but scored only limited sales success in markets such as Latvia, Lithuania, Spain and some South American countries. The weapons of the two Baltic states were taken over by the Soviet Union, after its 1939 annexation of these nations, for second-line service with the designation Rutschnoi pulemet "Vickers-Berthier".

Another development of the Vickers-Berthier machine gun was the Vickers G.O. (Gas Operated) or "K" gun with a 96-round drum magazine, which was used mainly as a trainable aeroplane gun until replaced by the Browning gun. Weapons made surplus to Royal Air Force requirement by this process found a second life in airfield defence or on vehicles employed in the North African campaign of 1940–43, especially those of units such as the Long-Range Desert Group and the Special Air Service.

SPECIFICATIONS

VICKERS-BERTHIER

Type:
light air-cooled machine gun

Calibre:
7.7mm (0.303in)

Length:
1.156m (45.5in)

Length of barrel:
0.60m (23.6in)

Weight:
10.9kg (24.4lb)

Muzzle velocity:
747m (2450ft) per second

Feed:
30-round round curved box magazine (450–600rpm)

VICKERS .303 MK I

<table>
<tr><th colspan="2">SPECIFICATIONS</th></tr>
</table>

VICKERS .303 MK I

Type:
heavy water-cooled machine gun

Calibre:
7.7mm (0.303in)

Length:
1.156m (45.5in)

Length of barrel:
0.721m (28.4in)

Weight:
18.1kg (40lb) for the gun with cooling water

Muzzle velocity:
744m (2440ft) per second

Feed:
250-round fabric belt (450–500rpm)

The Vickers Machine Gun Mk I entered service in 1912 and throughout its long production life remained essentially unaltered. The weapon was based on the Maxim gas-operated mechanism in an inverted form, and detail changes were introduced to create an extremely sturdy and reliable weapon that served the British and Commonwealth armies with great success in World Wars I and II. The weapon also achieved considerable export success to nations such as Latvia, Lithuania, the Netherlands, Russia and the USA. A few small changes were introduced over the weapon's production life, these variations including a smooth rather than corrugated water jacket, and differences in the muzzle recoil booster. Another mid-life change came with the introduction of the Mk 7z or Mk 8z nitrocellulose-loaded ammunition, which added another 915m (1000 yards) of range to the figure of 3290m (3600 yards) achieved with the original Mk 7 cordite-loaded ammunition, and suggested the adoption in 1942 of an optional dial sight for indirect fire. In World War I the US Army adopted the Vickers gun in 7.62mm (0.3in) calibre as the M1915, and in 1940 the 7000 or so surviving guns were sold back to the UK. The Germans designated captured British, Dutch and Soviet guns 7.7mm s MG 230(e), Dutch 7.7mm s MG 231(h) and 7.7mm s MG 230(r), respectively.

LEWIS GUN

The Lewis light machine gun was created by an American, Samuel McClean, but developed and marketed by another American, Colonel Isaac Lewis, and then first placed in production in Belgium and the UK prior to World War I before finally entering US manufacture during that war.

The Lewis gun was developed as an infantry weapon with a forced-draft cooling system, but was also used in aircraft with the barrel jacket removed as the slipstream served to cool the weapon. Between the two world wars the Lewis gun was produced in Belgium, France, Japan, the UK and the USA, and was widely exported. On the outbreak of World War II in 1939 the Lewis gun was still in very widespread service, and saw extensive use as the armament of merchant ships, for the defence of fixed land installations in single, double and quadruple mountings, and on the vehicles of special forces units, especially in North Africa.

The Germans used captured weapons including (German designation in parentheses) the British 7.7mm Lewis Gun Mk I (7.7mm le MG 137[e]), Dutch 6.5mm Mitrailleur M20 (6.5mm le MG 100[h]) and Soviet 7.62mm Rutschnoi pulemet "Lewis" (7.62mm le MG 122[r]). The Lewis was an excellent weapon, being both reliable and robust.

SPECIFICATIONS

LEWIS GUN

Type:
light air-cooled machine gun

Calibre:
7.7mm (0.303in)

Length:
1.25m (49.2in)

Length of barrel:
0.661m (26.04in)

Weight:
12.15kg (27lb)

Muzzle velocity:
744m (2440ft) per second

Feed:
47- or 97-round overhead drum magazine (450rpm)

PISTOLA M1889

SPECIFICATIONS

PISTOLA M1889

Type:
  revolver pistol

Calibre:
  10.35mm (0.4075in)

Length:
  0.23m (9.07in)

Length of barrel:
  0.122m (4.79in)

Weight:
  0.91kg (2lb)

Muzzle velocity:
  255m (837ft) per second

Feed:
  6-round revolving cylinder

There can be little doubt that the Pistola a Rotazione modello 1889 must have been in concept, if not necessarily in manufacture, one of the oldest types of pistol still in service in June 1940, when Italy entered World War II as one of the Axis powers. Although the weapon was introduced to Italian service in 1889, it was in fact derived from a revolver first issued to the Italian army in 1872. The modello 1889 was a sturdy and reliable rather than inspired revolver, and was retained in production right into the 1920s: there was no single source for the type, although the largest number was produced by Glisenti, so there were a number of detail differences between the revolvers manufactured by different companies.

It is possible that there were some 60 variations, large and small, and the most evident of these was in the region of the trigger. Here the modello 1889 could be found with a folding trigger and no trigger guard, or alternatively with a fixed trigger and trigger guard. Other elements in which they were variations were in the materials, the shaping of the hammer, the shaping of the butt, and the precise nature of the safety system used. Despite its obsolete nature, the modello 1889 was widely used by the Italian Army in every theatre in which Italian forces were involved.

BERETTA M1934

The first semi-automatic pistol by the celebrated Pietro Beretta SpA company of Italy was the modello 1915, which entered service with the Italian Army in the year in which Italy entered World War I as one of the Allied powers. This pioneering weapon was succeeded by the modello 1922 in 7.65mm calibre, the modello 1923 that was the first Beretta semi-automatic pistol with an external hammer and fired a 9mm round of the low-powered Glisenti type, and then the modello 1931 in 7.65mm calibre with a straighter grip and intended for use mainly by the Italian Navy.

These paved the way to the Pistola Automatica Beretta modello 1934 (specification at right), which was taken into large-scale service as the Italian Army's standard semi-automatic pistol of World War II. This gun was generally manufactured in 9mm calibre, the round being of the 9mm modello 1934 *corto* (short) type, but small numbers were completed in 7.65mm calibre. The modello 1934 was invariably finished to a very high standard, and after their seizure of northern Italy after September 1943 the Germans took into service all the weapons they could with the revised designation 9mm Pistole 671(i). A smaller and lighter version of the modello 1934 was produced as the 7.65mm modello 35 for the Italian Air Force.

SPECIFICATIONS

BERETTA M1934

Type:
semi-automatic pistol

Calibre:
9mm (0.354in) modello 1934 corto

Length:
0.152m (6in)

Length of barrel:
0.0865m (3.4in)

Weight:
0.617kg (1.36lb)

Muzzle velocity:
245m (804ft) per second

Feed:
7-round detachable straight box magazine

FUCILE M91

SPECIFICATIONS

FUCILE M91

Type:
  bolt-action rifle

Calibre:
  6.5mm (0.256in)

Length:
  1.285m (50.6in)

Length of barrel:
  0.78m (30.7in)

Weight:
  3.8kg (8.4lb)

Muzzle velocity:
  630m (2,067ft) per second

Feed:
  6-rounded fixed box magazine

The Fucile modello 91 was the first rifle of the Mauser-Paravicino or Mannlicher-Carcano type (Mauser one-piece bolt with front locking lugs and Mannlicher integral magazine loaded by means of a six-round clip that remained in the magazine until the last round was chambered) to be taken into service with the Italian Army. This took place in 1892, and the bolt action was that of the Mauser Gewehr 1889 modified with a Carcano bolt-sleeve safety mechanism, while Paravicino was the name of the general heading the commission that selected the weapon.

The modello 91 was the Italian Army's standard rifle right throughout the whole of World War I, and was still in large-scale service when Italy entered World War II in June 1940, when Mussolini invaded France. The Germans seized numbers of these rifles from September 1943 to equip elements for their forces in Italy, the revised designation being Gewehr 214(i), and in 1944 rebored small numbers to take the German standard 7.92mm round. Yugoslavia had also bought the modello 91 for service as the Puska 6.5mm M91, and the Germans used captured examples with the designation Gewehr 214(j). In 1905, Japan secured limited numbers of a modello 91 in a Rifle Type I variant chambered for the Japanese 6.5mm round.

FUCILE M38

The Fucile modello 38 has the distinction of being the first rifle created for a new Italian 7.35mm cartridge. The rifle was in fact a straightforward development of the 6.5mm modello 91 weapon with a larger-calibre barrel and modified sights. The weapon entered service in 1938, but the Italian authorities realized at this point that Italy's entry into a general European war could no longer be delayed.

Given the availability of vast quantities of 6.5mm ammunition already available, the decision was then made to revise the modello 38 to fire the older type of cartridge: most (but not all) of the existing rifles were fitted with a new barrel, and new-production weapons were produced in the smaller calibre. The inevitable result was a logistic nightmare that was still affecting the Italian Army up to the time of Italy's September 1943 armistice with the Allies.

Following Italy's exit from the war, the Germans took over stocks of the weapons for use with the designations 6.5mm Gewehr 209(i) and 7.35mm Gewehr 231(i). The Germans also tried to resolve the calibre problem by reboring weapons to 7.92mm calibre, but the power of the German cartridge meant that the resulting weapon was not safe. There was also a carbine version known as the Moschetto modello 1938 per cavalleria.

SPECIFICATIONS

FUCILE M38

Type:
  bolt-action rifle

Calibre:
  6.5 and 7.35mm (0.256 and 0.289in)

Length:
  1.02m (40.2in)

Length of barrel:
  0.54m (21.1in)

Weight:
  3.45kg (7.6lb)

Muzzle velocity:
  707m (2320ft) per second

Feed:
  6-round fixed straight box magazine

BERETTA M1918

SPECIFICATIONS

BERETTA M1918

Type:
  submachine gun

Calibre:
  9mm (0.354in) Glisenti

Length:
  0.85m (33.5in)

Length of barrel:
  0.317m (12.5in)

Weight:
  3.27kg (7.2lb)

Muzzle velocity:
  390m (1280ft) per second

Feed:
  25-round detachable box magazine (900rpm)

The world's first submachine gun, entering service in 1915, was the Villar Perosa that comprised a pair of weapons mounted on a vehicle pintle or shoulder-supported tray and controlled by means of spade grips to the sides of the thumb trigger mechanism. After World War I the Villar Perosa was developed for shoulder-fired use as the Officine Villar Perosa single-barrel weapon with a wooden stock and a conventional trigger. However, before the end of the war Tullio Marengoni of the Beretta company of Brescia in northern Italy had already created a more practical weapon, based on the same type of retarded blowback mechanism as the Villar Perosa and firing the same 9mm Glisenti low-powered round, as the Moschetto Automatico Beretta modello 1918 (see specification). The modello 1918 had a full set of wooden furniture, a completely new trigger arrangement, a modified operating mechanism to slow the rate of fire, and even a folding bayonet. The modello 1918 was also manufactured in two variants, one of them with a pair of triggers (for automatic and single-shot fire) and one with a single trigger for semi-automatic fire only. The modello 1918 drew its ammunition from an overhead magazine, but the modello 1918/30 was a revision firing the higher-powered 9mm Parabellum round from a magazine shifted through 180° to a position directly under the weapon.

BERETTA M38

Designed by Tullio Marengoni of the Beretta company and accepted for service in 1938, the Moschetto Automatico modello 38A was one of the company's most successful products. The weapon had good performance and was also very reliable as a result of its good design and the excellence with which it was manufactured. The first weapons of this type were chambered for a special round, the 9mm *cartucchia pallottola modello* 38A, but the demands of a growing number of export customers, especially in South America, for a variant using the more readily available 9mm Parabellum round meant that later weapons were chambered for this cartridge.

The type was also sold to Romania, and Germany used the weapon from 1941 with the designation 9mm Maschinenpistole 739(i). The modello 38A had four primary subvariants, none of them dignified by a particular designation. The first had provision for a bayonet and featured a compensator on the muzzle; the second had a barrel jacket in which the original slots were replaced by circular holes; the third appeared late in 1938 without provision for a bayonet and featuring a four-slot compensator; and the fourth appeared late in 1940 as a more easily produced type with a barrel jacket welded from stampings.

SPECIFICATIONS

BERETTA M38

Type:
submachine gun

Calibre:
9mm (0.354in)

Length:
0.947m (37.3in)

Length of barrel:
0.32m (12.6in)

Weight:
3.945kg (8.7lb)

Muzzle velocity:
450m (1476ft) per second

Feed:
10-, 20- or 40-round box magazine (550–600rpm)

BERETTA M38/42

SPECIFICATIONS

BERETTA M38/42

Type:
submachine gun

Calibre:
9mm (0.354in) Parabellum

Length:
0.80m (31.5in)

Length of barrel:
0.20m (7.87in)

Weight:
3.27kg (7.2lb)

Muzzle velocity:
450m (1476ft) per second

Feed:
20- or 40-round detachable box magazine (550rpm)

In service the Beretta modello 38A submachine gun revealed itself to be a first-class weapon of its type, but it also became abundantly clear that the modello 38A was not suited in production and cost terms to large-scale manufacture under the increasingly austere conditions imposed on Italy by World War II. Beretta therefore undertook the task of simplifying the modello 38A into a weapon that offered basically unaltered operational capabilities but was easier and therefore cheaper to make. The result was the Moschetto Automatico Beretta modello 38/42 (see specification at left). This made use of stamped steel components wherever possible, had no barrel jacket, fired 9mm ammunition of the Parabellum rather than lower-powered Glisenti type, and was provided with a new form of dust-protected bolt to improve reliability under adverse conditions such as those found in the North African campaign and the Italian sector of the Eastern Front. Even so, the modello 38/42 still emerged as a weapon of notably high quality that was used by the Italians, Romanians and Germans, the last of whom issued the 9mm Maschinenpistole 738(i) to their forces in Italy and North Africa. The modelli 38/43 and 38/44 were later variants with further changes to speed and cheapen manufacture still further.

FIAT M14

I taly's standard machine gun of World War I was the 6.5mm Revelli modello 1914 manufactured mostly by Fiat and often known as the Fiat-Revelli. From 1935 significant numbers of these obsolescent weapons were improved to Mitriaglice Fiat modello 1914/35 standard, with guns built to the same standard receiving the designation modello 35. The primary alteration was effected in the feed system, in which the original Revelli type of 50-round magazine divided into 10 five-round compartments was replaced by a belt feed, but another major change was the replacement of the original water-cooled barrel by a heavier air-cooled barrel of the quick-change type in the new Italian calibre of 8mm. It was hoped that the changes (including a fluted chamber) would remove the need for the cartridge-oiling system used in the modello 14 to facilitate the extraction of spent cartridges, but this cumbersome and dirt-attracting system had in fact to be retained.

The modello 1914/35 was actually a worse gun than the modello 1914, one of its poorest features being the tendency of the barrel to overheat very rapidly. Even so, the modello 1914/35 was retained through World War II for lack of an adequate replacement, and the Germans used small numbers of this poor weapon with the designation 8mm s MG 255(i).

SPECIFICATIONS

FIAT M14

Type:
  medium air-cooled machine gun

Calibre:
  8mm (0.315in)

Length:
  1.2635m (49.75in)

Length of barrel:
  0.654m (25.75in)

Weight:
  17.9kg (39.75lb) gun; 18.7kg (41.5lb) for the tripod

Muzzle velocity:
  790m (2592ft) per second

Feed:
  300-round non-disintegrating belt (500rpm)

BREDA M30

SPECIFICATIONS

BREDA M30

Type:
light air-cooled machine gun

Calibre:
6.5mm (0.256in)

Length:
1.232m (48.5in)

Length of barrel:
0.520m (20.5in)

Weight:
10.24kg (22.75lb)

Muzzle velocity:
630m (2067ft) per second

Feed:
20-round fixed straight box magazine (450–500rpm)

The 6.5mm Fucile Mitriagliatori Breda modello 30 was a light machine gun evolved via the modello 1924, modello 1928 and modello 1929 weapons of the same type, and served through Italy's involvement in World War II as the Italian Army's standard light machine gun. In many respects the modello 1930 was a distinctly poor weapon, but for lack of any viable alternative it was retained in service and saw extensive use, especially in the see-saw campaign waged in North Africa. Like the Revelli modello 1914, the modello 1930 was of the delayed blowback type with a recoiling barrel and a massive bolt carrying several locking lugs, and this demanded the use of an oiling mechanism to lubricate the cartridge cases, before they were loaded, so that adequate extraction of spent cases could be achieved: the oiler attracted significant quantities of dirt and dust, especially under North African conditions, and this was the cause of repeated jammings. Two other poor features of the design were the magazine and quick-change barrel. The magazine was permanently attached to the right-hand side of the weapon by a hinge that allowed the unit to be swung forward for loading: any damage or distortion of this magazine rendered the modello 1930 inoperative. The barrel lacked a handle, which meant that barrel changing was singularly slow.

BREDA M37

Created as the successor to the modello 1914/35, the Mitriaglice Breda modello 37 (see specification) emerged in World War II as the best Italian heavy machine gun for land-based service. A significant improvement was effected over the earlier weapon in the use of gas rather than delayed blowback operation, but a system to oil the cartridges was still employed and the feed system was decidedly odd as rounds were fed into the gun from a 20-round flat tray into which the spent cases were then returned: this meant that the spent cases then had to be dumped before the magazine could be reloaded. Even so, the modello 37 proved itself a sturdy and reliable weapon, qualities that endeared it to the troops in the field, especially those fighting in the heat of North Africa or on the freezing steppes of Russia, and the type could be installed on a tall tripod mounting for use in the anti-aircraft role.

The Germans operated limited numbers of modello 37 machine guns with the designation 8mm s MG 259(i). The modello 37 was also developed into a variant for use in armoured fighting vehicles. Entering service in 1938, this Mitriaglice Breda calibro 8 modello 38 per carri armati (known to the Germans as the 8mm Kpfw MG 350[i]) had a conventional curved box magazine above the weapon, and was generally mounted on assault guns.

SPECIFICATIONS

BREDA M37

Type:
heavy air-cooled machine gun

Calibre:
8mm (0.315in)

Length:
1.27m (50in)

Length of barrel:
0.74m (29.1in)

Weight:
19.3kg (42.8lb) gun; 18.7kg (41.5lb) tripod mounting

Muzzle velocity:
790m (2592ft) per second

Feed:
20-round strip (450rpm)

PISTOL TYPE 26

SPECIFICATIONS

PISTOL TYPE 26

Type:
revolver pistol

Calibre:
9mm (0.354in)

Length:
0.24m (9.4in)

Length of barrel:
0.12m (4.7in)

Weight:
0.9kg (2lb)

Muzzle velocity:
275m (902ft) per second

Feed:
6-round cylinder

The Revolver Pistol Type 26 weapon entered service, initially with cavalry units of the Imperial Japanese Army, in the course of 1893. The design of this revolver blended a number of American and European design features, including break-open access to the cylinder typical of the American Smith & Wesson company and lock work derived from that of the Austro-Hungarian Rast and Gasser.

The revolver had two notably unusual features in being double-action only (in the fashion of later British-designed 0.38in/9.65mm Enfield revolvers) and chambered for a unique 9mm rimmed pistol round. One good feature of the design was its hinged side plate, which provided easy access to the lock work. From 1925 this indifferent revolver was replaced as the Japanese Army's standard pistol by a semi-automatic weapon, but despite this fact remained in large-scale service and was widely used in World War II. Like many revolvers of its type, this weapon was very sturdy, and could operate in inhospitable terrain. In addition – and this was very important to Japanese troops operating in the Pacific on islands that were often far from workshops – it was easy to maintain: it could be stripped and re-assembled very quickly (it had relatively few working parts).

PISTOL TYPE 14

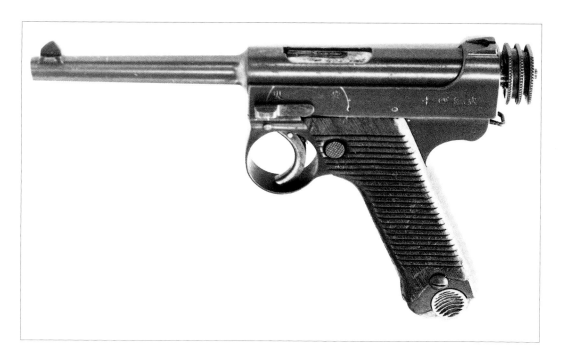

Introduced in 1925, the Pistol Type 14 pistol was designed by Colonel Kijiro Nambu and manufactured by the Kayoba Factory Co. Ltd. as the specifically military version of Nambu's 8mm Pistol Type 1904. The 1904 model had been created for the commercial market, but even so had secured major sales to Japanese officers wanting a pistol more advanced than the Type 26 revolver (see page opposite).

By comparison with the Type 1904, the Type 14 had a manual rather than grip safety, a magazine with a safety, and a rear sight of the fixed notch rather than tangent type and, as a more obvious external difference, a narrower butt. The mechanism was also modified slightly, and the weapon's construction was beefed-up for service use. These modifications could not conceal the fact, however, that the Type 14 was still an indifferent pistol that was altogether too prone to reliability problems. The Type 14 (Modified), which was introduced in 1938, was fitted with a larger trigger guard to allow the weapon's use by men wearing gloves. More modern designs, of course, usually meant more working parts and more intricate working mechanisms. These were fine on ranges and on the parade ground, but in the mud and grime of battle they were found wanting – with often fatal results for the user.

SPECIFICATIONS

PISTOL TYPE 14

Type:
semi-automatic pistol

Calibre:
8mm (0.315in)

Length:
0.23m (9in)

Length of barrel:
0.12m (4.75in)

Weight:
0.91kg (2lb)

Muzzle velocity:
325m (1066ft) per second

Feed:
8-round detachable straight box magazine

PISTOL TYPE 94

SPECIFICATIONS

PISTOL TYPE 94

Type:
  semi-automatic pistol

Calibre:
  8mm (0.315in)

Length:
  0.183m (7.2in)

Length of barrel:
  0.096m (3.8in)

Weight:
  0.766kg (1.69lb)

Muzzle velocity:
  325m (1066ft) per second

Feed:
  6-round detachable straight box magazine

Arguably one of the worst if not actually the worst semi-automatic pistol ever placed in full military service, the Type 94 pistol was introduced in 1934 and, securing virtually no civil sales, was manufactured in the Japanese Army's own arsenals as the side arm of the Imperial Japanese Army's officers. Service use very rapidly revealed the extent of the weapon's deficiencies, which included an acute lack of "pointability", a sear that was exposed on the left-hand side of the receiver in a fashion that allowed it to be jolted and so discharge the weapon, and a locking mechanism that allowed the weapon to be fired without the receiver being locked, especially if poor maintenance had allowed the relevant parts to be worn down.

All these factors were bad enough when the pistol was manufactured under peace-time conditions, but the situation became worse still after Japan's December 1941 entry into World War II resulted in a steady degradation of quality control to the extent that late-production examples of the Type 14 were as dangerous to the firer as the target it was being aimed at! Work on the design of a replacement pistol was launched in 1942 and resulted in the Type 11 pistol, but progress was slow and only some 500 of these guns had been completed before Japan's defeat in 1945.

RIFLE TYPE 38

The Rifle Type 38 was an evolutionary development of the Rifle Type 30 designed by Colonel Arisaka, and was thus often known by the Japanese as the Arisaka Rifle. The Type 30 (and thus the Type 38) was based on the Mauser bolt action as exemplified in the Gewehr 98 but modified in elements of its cocking (during the forward movement of the bolt as on the Lee Enfield) and its safety (the Mauser type of flag-type safety being replaced by a knob on the rear of the bolt that was pushed in and turned to lock the firing pin).

The Type 38 fired a relatively low-powered cartridge, and in combination with a long barrel this resulted in low recoil forces, which was a factor that suited the generally small size and light weight of the average Japanese infantryman. However, the length of the rifle made the Type 38 a weapon difficult to handle, especially after the long Type 30 bayonet had been fitted, which the Japanese always favoured.

The Type 38 was the standard Japanese Army rifle in the period after the end of the Russo-Japanese War in 1905, and remained in service right through to the end of World War II. The weapon was also exported to Siam (later Thailand). Adopted in 1937, the Type 97 was a sniper version of the Type 38. Overall it was a reliable and robust weapon.

SPECIFICATIONS

RIFLE TYPE 38

Type:
bolt-action rifle

Calibre:
6.5mm (0.256in)

Length:
1.275m (50.2in)

Length of barrel:
0.7975m (31.4in)

Weight:
4.2kg (9.25lb)

Muzzle velocity:
730m (2395ft) per second

Feed:
5-round fixed box magazine

CARBINE TYPE 38

SPECIFICATIONS

CARBINE TYPE 38

Type:
bolt-action carbine

Calibre:
6.5mm (0.256in)

Length:
0.869m (34.2in)

Length of barrel:
0.506m (19.9in)

Weight:
3.3kg (7.3lb)

Muzzle velocity:
700m (2297ft) per second

Feed:
5-round fixed box magazine

An exact contemporary of the Rifle Type 38, being introduced to service in 1905, the Carbine Type 38 was basically similar to the rifle and differed significantly only in the length of its barrel. The weapon was intended for service with mounted troops, but with the decline of this branch of the Imperial Japanese Army during the 1930s the Carbine Type 38 was by 1941 the weapon mainly of second-line forces and also with the garrisons of fixed installations, including fortress areas. Like the Rifle Type 38, the Carbine Type 38 was also captured in large enough numbers by the Chinese to equip several formations. It is curious that this weapon was not adopted in greater numbers by Japanese frontline formations, as its performance was only marginally less than the longer Type 38. No doubt the psychological effect that the longer rifles with bayonets attached had on the enemy had something to do with the choice of weapon.

The shorter length and lower weight of the Carbine Type 38 by comparison with the Rifle Type 38 also commended the Carbine Type 38 as the basis for the personal weapon of the Japanese airborne forces, which received limited numbers of a version with a butt that was hinged to fold to the right as a means of reducing length still further.

RIFLE TYPE 99

From 1932 Japanese forces gradually adopted a heavier 7.7mm cartridge for use in the Type 92 machine gun, and in 1939 a rimless derivative of this cartridge was introduced, despite the fact that the higher recoil forces were difficult for the average Japanese soldier to handle, as the ammunition for an improved Rifle Type 99 version of the Type 38 rifle. The opportunity was taken to introduce a number of other changes, these including a rear sight designed to provide anti-aircraft capability through the addition of folding lateral arms marked off for speed "lead", a folding wire monopod, and alterations designed to ease production.

As the effects of World War II on Japanese war industries became more acute, further changes were introduced (including a conventional rear sight) to simplify production with poorer materials and less skilled manpower, and from 1943 the weapon was decidedly crude in manufacture and finish. There were two models which differed only in barrel length (the specification applies to the shorter-barrel model), and another model was made for airborne troops. This last model could be broken into two sections (connected by a spring-loaded plunger) by means of an interrupted thread in the barrel just forward of the receiver, and had a bolt handle that could be removed.

SPECIFICATIONS

RIFLE TYPE 99

Type:
bolt-action rifle

Calibre:
7.7mm (0.303in)

Length:
1.275m (50.1in)

Length of barrel:
0.655m (25.8in)

Weight:
3.9kg (8.6lb)

Muzzle velocity:
730m (2395ft) per second

Feed:
5-round fixed box magazine

SMG TYPE 100

SPECIFICATIONS

SMG TYPE 100

Type:
  submachine gun

Calibre:
  8mm (0.315in)

Length:
  0.867m (34in) butt extended; 0.564m (22.2in) folded

Length of barrel:
  0.228m (9in)

Weight:
  3.83kg (8.5lb)

Muzzle velocity:
  335m (1099ft) per second

Feed:
  30-round detachable box magazine (450rpm)

Japan was initially less enthusiastic about the capabilities of the submachine gun than the armies of the Western world, and up to the late 1930s the Imperial Japanese Army was content to import Bergmann Model 1920 weapons from Switzerland in limited numbers for evaluation and the equipment of some small special forces units. In 1940, however, the Japanese introduced their first submachine gun of indigenous design, the Sub-Machine Gun Type 100 created by the army's own ordnance branch under the supervision of General Kijiro Nambu. The Type 100 was manufactured in three forms, one with a fixed butt, a bayonet lug bar and sometimes a compensator, one with a folding butt and bayonet lug bar (see specification) for airborne forces, and one delivered from 1944 as a simplified weapon with a fixed butt, a bayonet lug on the barrel jacket, a compensator and a fixed-aperture rear sight.

All three variants of the Type 100 fired the Japanese 8mm pistol round, and were capable of automatic fire only. The design could be regarded most charitably as indifferent, and the service use of the weapon was bedevilled by the poor quality of the ammunition. Production amounted to perhaps 10,000 and 7500 examples of the fixed- and folding-butt variants respectively.

HMG TYPE 3

Impressed with the capabilities of the Hotchkiss modèle 1900 heavy machine gun, of which it had used small numbers in the Russo-Japanese War of 1904–05, the Imperial Japanese Army decided to order a locally developed version optimized for Japanese manufacturing techniques. The result was the Heavy Machine Gun Type 3 that was adopted in 1914 as a development of the baseline French weapon with the calibre altered from 8mm to 6.5mm and the modifications effected in the ejector system.

The Type 3 was the standard heavy machine gun of the Japanese Army for many years, and in overall configuration was very similar to the French original except in features such as fittings at the base of the tripod legs for the insertion of carrying poles, more cooling fins on the barrel, and an oiling mechanism to lubricate the cartridges as they were fed into the gun from the Hotchkiss type of ammunition strip.

The Japanese forces still had large numbers of the Type 3 machine gun in their inventories in 1941, and though forces in the field appreciated the weapon's basic soundness and reliability, they were less favourably disposed to its poor range and low stopping power with the 6.5mm round, as well as the inadequate 30-round ammunition strips it fired.

SPECIFICATIONS

HMG TYPE 3

Type:
heavy air-cooled machine gun

Calibre:
6.5mm (0.256in)

Length:
1.37m (45.5in)

Length of barrel:
0.745m (29.2in)

Weight:
28.1kg (62lb) gun; 27.2kg (60lb) tripod mounting

Muzzle velocity:
745m (2444ft) per second

Feed:
30-round metal strips (400–500rpm)

LMG TYPE 11

SPECIFICATIONS

LMG TYPE 11

Type:
  light air-cooled machine gun

Calibre:
  6.5mm (0.256in)

Length:
  1.105m (43.5in)

Length of barrel:
  0.483m (19in)

Weight:
  10.1kg (22.5lb)

Muzzle velocity:
  700m (2297ft) per second

Feed:
  30-round hopper using six 5-round clips (500rpm)

The Light Machine Gun Type 11 entered service with the Imperial Japanese Army in the course of 1922 and its design, though modelled on Hotchkiss thinking, was unusual in many ways. The weapon was designed by General Kijiro Nambu and was still the infantry's standard light machine gun when Japan entered World War II in December 1941. The weapon remained in service throughout Japan's involvement in World War II even though superior machine guns were created to replace it.

The Type 11 machine gun had an unusual feed arrangement in the form of a hopper filled with a stack of standard rifle ammunition clips as used by Japanese infantrymen: the concept was sound, but in practice the mechanism was too complex for effective field use and therefore presented problems that could be solved only by the introduction of a lower-powered round, resulting in generally reduced overall performance.

Despite its numerous shortcomings, the Type 11 light machine gun saw very extensive service. The weapon possessed a very distinctive butt attached to the rear of the trigger guard and the underside of the receiver, and could be fired from either in inbuilt bipod (as shown in the above photograph) or, for the sustained-fire role, a tripod mounting.

LMG TYPE 96

Entering service in 1936, the Light Machine Gun Type 96 was conceived and developed as the successor to the indifferent and obsolescent Light Machine Gun Type 11, but Japanese production under wartime conditions was so slow that the new weapon in fact supplemented rather than supplanted the older machine gun. The Type 96 was of modern concept by the standards of the day, and combined features which the Japanese design team copied from the French Hotchkiss and Czechoslovak ZB vz.26 weapon.

One of the most important conceptual changes in the Type 96 was the replacement of the Type 11's hopper feed system with an overhead box magazine of the Czechoslovak type, but even though the reduced-power Type 30 cartridge was used, the Type 96 had to keep the Type 11's type of cartridge-lubrication system with all its dirt-catching propensities. Two good features were the introduction of a quick-change barrel capability, and the facility to use either drum or telescopic sights. Another feature, and one perhaps unique among service machine guns, was the provision for a bayonet. This was a peculiar Japanese trait, and was totally useless as the task of machine guns was to support charging infantrymen as they made their bayonet attacks, rather than running alongside them.

SPECIFICATIONS

LMG TYPE 96

Type:
  light air-cooled machine gun

Calibre:
  6.5mm (0.256in)

Length:
  1.055m (41.5in)

Barrel length:
  0.55m (21.65in)

Weight:
  9.07kg (20lb)

Muzzle velocity:
  730m (2395ft) per second

Feed:
  30-round detachable curved magazine (550rpm)

HMG TYPE 92

SPECIFICATIONS

HMG TYPE 92

Type:
heavy air-cooled machine gun

Calibre:
7.7mm (0.303in)

Length:
1.156m (45.5in)

Length of barrel:
0.749mm (29.5in)

Weight:
55.3kg (122lb) with tripod mounting

Muzzle velocity:
730m (2395ft) per second

Feed:
30-round metal strip (450–500rpm)

The tactical limitations of the relatively low-powered 6.5mm rifle cartridge were appreciated by the Japanese during and after World War I, and in 1932 the Japanese ammunition development service pioneered a more powerful 7.7mm round offering longer range and greater hitting power throughout its range bracket.

Of the new weapons produced to exploit the capabilities of the new round, one of the first was the Heavy Machine Gun Type 92 that was standardized in 1932. This was in effect a reworking of the Imperial Japanese Army's current heavy machine gun, the Type 3, in the larger calibre. For reasons that remain unexplained, the opportunity was not taken in the development of the Type 92 to remove two of the Type 3's main disadvantages, namely the oil lubrication mechanism for the cartridges before they entered the gun, and the Hotchkiss type of strip feed.

The Type 92 became the Japanese Army's standard heavy machine gun and remained in service throughout World War II, in which it was supplemented by the Heavy Machine Gun Type 1, a lightened version with a shorter barrel. This weapon was robust and reliable overall, and served throughout Word War II, giving frontline troops sound machine-gun support.

LMG TYPE 99

The Light Machine Gun Type 99 was the best Japanese machine gun used in World War II after being introduced in 1939. The Type 99 weapon was developed from the 6.5mm Type 96, in a fashion analogous to the evolution of the Type 92 heavy machine gun from the Type 3 weapon, to use the new and somewhat higher-powered 7.7mm round in its definitive Type 99 rimless form. The Type 99 was a more fully optimized weapon than the Type 92, however, and the use of the rimless round meant that the system for oil lubrication of fresh rounds could be omitted. The standard bipod arrangement towards the front of the barrel was retained, and supplemented in the new weapon by an adjustable monopod under the butt's heel for greater stability when the gun was being fired at a long-range target. In other respects the Type 96 and Type 99 weapon were essentially identical, to the extent that even the entirely superfluous bayonet fitting was retained. There was also a Parachute Type Machine Gun Type 92 for the use of airborne forces: this could be broken down into three parts for ease of movement. Unfortunately for the men of the Imperial Japanese Army, production of the Type 99 machine gun never reached the figure that would have allowed the replacement of all its older light machine guns.

SPECIFICATIONS

LMG TYPE 99

Type:
light air-cooled machine gun

Calibre:
7.7mm (0.303in)

Length:
1.19m (46.75in)

Length of barrel:
0.545m (21.5in)

Weight:
10.4kg (23lb)

Muzzle velocity:
715m (2346ft) per second

Feed:
30-round detachable box magazine (850rpm)

GEVAER M/1894

SPECIFICATIONS

GEVAER M/1894

Type:
bolt-action rifle

Calibre:
6.5mm (0.256in)

Length:
1.27m (49.9in)

Length of barrel:
0.765mm (30.1in)

Weight:
4.05kg (8.9lb)

Muzzle velocity:
about 800m (2625ft) per second

Feed:
5-round detachable straight box magazine

The first service rifle based on the indigenous Krag-Jorgensen bolt action and righthand-side magazine to enter Norwegian service was the Gevaer m/1894 firing a Mauser 6.5mm rimless cartridge. Production of this weapon was initially undertaken both in Austria-Hungary (by Steyr) and in Norway (by the Kongsberg arsenal), but the majority of the rifles were made in Norway. The m/1894 was without doubt a capable and reliable weapon that was excellently made of high-quality materials, and was still the Norwegian Army's standard rifle at the time Germany overran Norway between April and June 1940.

The Germans then seized the surviving weapons for service with the revised designation 6.5mm Gewehr 211(n). The rifle was also produced in sniper and carbine versions. For sniping there were the Skarpskyttergevaer m/1923 with a telescopic sight to the left of the bolt action, the Skarpskyttergevaer m/1925 differing only in the stock, and the Skarpskyttergevaer m/1930 which had the look of a sporting weapon as it lacked a forestock and had no provision for a bayonet.

The carbine variants were the m/1895, m/1897, m/1904, m/1907 and m/1912 that differed from each other mainly in their stocks and swivels. Overall this weapon was a robust one.

PISTOL M1911

The M1911 semi-automatic was first produced in 1911 by Colt to one of the classic designs by John M. Browning, who created the weapon as a short-range pistol capable of halting and throwing back a charging man. After that the pistol became one of the most important military sidearms ever produced.

The baseline M1911 was widely used in World War I, and an assessment of the weapon's performance in that conflict resulted, during 1926, in the introduction of the M1911A1 definitive model (specifications for this model are given in the table at right). This differed from its predecessor mainly in the shaping of the grip with finger cuts behind the trigger, the lengthening and smoothing of the trigger, the size of the grip safety, and the alteration of the rifling.

In World War II the M1911A1 was used by many Allied forces in addition to those of the USA, one of these other users being the UK where some of the weapons were revised to 11.56mm (0.455in) calibre. The pistol was also made under licence in countries such as Spain and Norway (11.25mm automatisk pistol modell 1914, later used by the Germans as the Pistole 657[n]). Other pistols used by the Germans received the generic designation P 660(a). This pistol is still in service in parts of the world.

SPECIFICATIONS

PISTOL M1911

Type:
semi-automatic pistol

Calibre:
11.43mm (0.45in)

Length:
0.218m (8.6in)

Length of barrel:
0.128m (5.03in)

Weight:
1.1kg (2.44lb)

Muzzle velocity:
262m (860ft) per second

Feed:
7-round detachable straight box magazine

SPRINGFIELD M1903

SPECIFICATIONS

SPRINGFIELD M1903

Type:
bolt-action rifle

Calibre:
7.62mm (0.3in)

Length:
1.105m (43.5in)

Length of barrel:
0.61m (24in)

Weight:
4.1kg (9lb)

Muzzle velocity:
855m (2805ft) per second

Feed:
5-round fixed box magazine

It was in 1903 that the US Army standardized as its infantry rifle a modified version of the short Mauser rifle, and this was generally known as the "Springfield" for the arsenal in which it was first manufactured. The Model 1903 had the look of a typical Mauser rifle but, being of the short type, could also be used by cavalry and second-line units. The M1903 was the USA's standard rifle in World War I and the period following it, but although the M1 semi-automatic rifle was standardized as its successor in the 1930s, the bolt-action rifle remained in large-scale service right up to the end of World War II in 1945. During the USA's involvement in World War II from December 1941 there were three primary variants of the M1903 in service. The M1903A1 was adopted in 1939 and had a pistol-grip stock and a serrated trigger. The M1903A3 was introduced in May 1942 with features such as stamped steel components and simplified sights to facilitate production. The M1903A4 was introduced in December 1942 as the sniper counterpart of the M1903A3 with a x2.5 telescopic sight and no iron sights. The M1903 rifle was delivered in large numbers to American allies, especially China, and numbers were also handed over to guerrilla forces in Burma and the Philippines. The Germans allocated small numbers of captured weapons, known by the designation 7.62mm Gewehr 239(a).

M1 RIFLE

The Rifle M1 was the first semi-automatic rifle to enter full service anywhere in the world, being standardized for US service in 1932. Despite a major production programme that saw the delivery by 1945 of more than 5.5 million such rifles, however, the weapon did not entirely supersede the M1903 in World War II. The M1 rifle was known to virtually every soldier as the "Garand" after its creator, John C. Garand.

The M1 rifle was a well-designed weapon that was always well manufactured in a process that was somewhat expensive but yielded a weapon that was effective and reliable. There was a large number of experimental models, but the other two production variants in addition to the standard rifle were the M1C and M1D sniper versions standardized in June and September 1944, respectively.

A gas-operated weapon, the M1 rifle was fed with ammunition from an eight-round magazine that retained the charger clip until the last round was fired: this meant that the magazine could not be topped up with single rounds, and that the distinctive sound of the clip's ejection signalled both the firer's position and the fact that his weapon was empty. The German Army used captured M1 rifles with the designation 7.62mm Selbstladegewehr 251(a).

SPECIFICATIONS

M1 RIFLE

Type:
semi-automatic rifle

Calibre:
7.62mm (0.3in)

Length:
1.107m (43.6in)

Length of barrel:
0.609m (24in)

Weight:
4.31kg (9.5lb)

Muzzle velocity:
855m (2805ft) per second

Feed:
8-round fixed magazine

M1 CARBINE

SPECIFICATIONS

M1 CARBINE

Type:
semi-automatic carbine

Calibre:
7.63mm (0.3in)

Length:
0.904m (35.6in)

Length of barrel:
0.457m (18in)

Weight:
2.36kg (5.2lb)

Muzzle velocity:
600m (1970ft) per second

Feed:
15- or 30-round detachable straight box magazine

In 1940 the US Army decided to adopt an automatic carbine to replace the pistol that had been the personal weapon of combat troops other than the infantry up to that time. Late in the same year there were trials of a number of contending weapons, of which a Winchester semi-automatic carbine emerged as the winner. This was standardized as the Carbine M1 (specifications for this weapon are given in the table at left), which had a unique gas-operated mechanism and in service revealed itself to be a very successful and popular weapon.

The M1 carbine was soon issued to frontline troops as well as its originally conceived recipients, and as a result production of this trim weapon exceeded 6.3 million units in Word War II – a figure greater than that of any other American weapon of the period. The one failing of the M1 carbine was its special cartridge, which lacked adequate power and therefore limited the carbine to short- and medium-range use.

The M1 carbine's sole major variant was the M1A1 with a folding stock for service with airborne troops. German special forces units used small numbers of captured carbines with the designation 7.63mm Selbstladekarabiner 455(a). The M1 carbine was one of the great weapons of World War II.

THOMPSON M1928

Designed in World War I, the submachine gun designed by J.T. Thompson did not enter production with the Auto-Ordnance Corporation until 1921. The Model 1921 was produced in some numbers as a retarded-blowback weapon chambered for the standard 11.43mm (0.45in) pistol cartridge carried in several types of magazine including a not very successful 100-round drum magazine but more commonly 50-round drum and 20-round vertical box magazines. The drum magazine model entered folklore as the weapon of American gangsters, a myth largely started and perpetuated by Hollywood.

The Model 1928 was a modest improvement with features such as the Cutts compensator (specifications for this weapon are given in the table at right) to help control muzzle climb. The US Navy bought small numbers, but in 1939 the British and French armies ordered large numbers. From June 1940 the French weapons were taken over by the Germans with the designation Maschinenpistole 760(f), and other such weapons entered the German inventory via the Baltic states, the USSR and Yugoslavia, whose weapons became MP 760(j) submachine guns. In the USA the Model 1928 was issued to cavalry units as the M1928A1. Overall this weapon was a very sound design.

SPECIFICATIONS

THOMPSON M1928

Type:
submachine gun

Calibre:
11.43mm (0.45in)

Length:
0.857m (33.75in)

Length of barrel:
0.267mm (10.52in)

Weight:
4.88kg (10.75lb)

Muzzle velocity:
280m (920ft) per second

Feed:
20- or 30-round box, or 50-round drum (600–725rpm)

SMG M1

SPECIFICATIONS

SMG M1

Type:
submachine gun

Calibre:
11.43mm (0.45in)

Length:
0.813m (32in)

Length of barrel:
0.267m (10.52in)

Weight:
4.74kg (10.45lb)

Muzzle velocity:
280m (920ft) per second

Feed:
20- or 30-round detachable box magazine (700rpm)

During the 1930s efforts were made to reduce the complexity, and thus the cost and manufacturing time, of the Model 1928. The weapon was therefore adapted with a more simple blowback operating system and the omission of features such as the compensator, the barrel cooling fins and the removable butt stock. European expedience had revealed the 50-round drum magazine to be noisy and too bulky, especially for use on the battlefield, so provision was made only for the two sizes of straight magazine. This resulted in the Gun, Sub-machine, Caliber .45, M1, of which more than one million had been completed before the end of World War II in 1945.

The M1A1 variant was the result of further simplification in which the original separate firing pin and hammer were replaced by a fixed firing pin. The M1 and M1A1 were often preferred by troops to later weapons such as the M3, and the types were delivered in large numbers to the forces of other Allied powers. The types were especially popular in the Far East, and the Chinese produced their own version to succeed their clone of the M1928A1. Its popularity stemmed from the fact that it was a very robust and reliable weapon, and could be easily maintained in the field – an absolute necessity for Chinese forces.

SMG M3

In 1942 the US Army trialled several types of sub-machine guns, but none of these fully met the service's requirement. The staff at the Aberdeen Proving Grounds then created a simple design as the T15, which was thoroughly tested and paved the way to the improved T20 that was standardized for service as the Gun, Sub-machine, Caliber .45, M3.

The M3 was modelled closely on the Sten gun, which had been evaluated in the USA, but introduced changes such as ammunition feed from a vertical 30-round box magazine based on that of a German weapon, the Maschinenpistole 40. Initial service reaction was lukewarm, but the M3 then became popular as it showed itself to be effective and reliable, being nicknamed the "Grease Gun".

Mass production requirements had been designed into the weapon, which made extensive use of stamped and forged components in place of machine items, and this meant that general engineering companics were able to deliver more than 600,000 of the weapons by the end of the war in 1945. The M3A1 was a development that took the simplification of the design a stage further, replaced the breakable bolt retraction handle with a finger hole in the bolt, and increased the size of the ejection port.

SPECIFICATIONS

SMG M3

Type:
submachine gun

Calibre:
11.43 mm (0.45in)

Length:
0.757m (29in) extended; 0.579m (22.8in) retracted

Length of barrel:
0.203m (8in)

Weight:
3.7kg (8.15lb)

Muzzle velocity:
about 280m (920ft) per second

Feed:
30-round detachable box magazine (350–450rpm)

BAR

SPECIFICATIONS

BAR

Type:
 light machine gun

Calibre:
 7.62mm (0.3in)

Length:
 1.214m (47.8in)

Length of Barrel :
 0.611m (24.07in)

Weight:
 8.73kg (19.4lb)

Muzzle velocity:
 808m (2650ft) per second

Feed:
 20-round detachable box magazine (300–350rpm)

While to the US forces the classic Browning Automatic Rifle, or BAR, was just that, to others the weapon was a light machine gun. The BAR was introduced to provide the US infantry involved in World War I with a weapon to bolster their firepower, and in World War II was the standard squad support weapon. The three primary models of this elegant weapon were the original Model 1918 hand-operated gun with no bipod but with a simple tube-type flash hider, the Model 1918A1 with a bipod and shoulder strap, and the Model 1918A2 (specification at left) with a butt monopod and the bipod (with plate rather than spiked feet) moved forwards from the front of the gas cylinder to the flash hider. The M1918A2 had two rates of automatic fire rather than the earlier models' selective fire capability, but this feature was sometimes removed. In Belgium the FN company also produced the BAR as its Fusil Mitrailleur modèle 1930 based on the M1918A1 and exported in 7, 7.65 and 7.92mm calibres. Captured Belgian weapons were used by the Germans with the designation 7.65mm le MG 727(b), while the 7.92mm Reczny karabin maszynowy wz.28 weapons seized in Poland became 7.9mm le MG 154(p) guns. Polish weapons seized by the USSR became 7.92mm Rutschnoi pulemet Browning obrazets 1928 guns.

M1917

Unlike other Browning automatic weapons of its period, the machine gun that entered service as the Machine Gun, Caliber .30in, M1917 was designed from the late 1890s with recoil rather than gas operation, and this was so successful that all subsequent Browning automatic weapons used the same system.

The M1917 looked similar to the Vickers gun except for its single pistol grip rather than twin spade grips, and large-scale production followed. The M1917, of which more than 68,000 were completed, was succeeded in 1936 by the M1917A1 (specifications for this particular model are given in the table at right) of which more than 54,000 were produced with changes in the sight, feed and tripod mounting, and this was the standard support machine gun operated by the US Army during World War II.

The Polish Ciezki karabin maszynowy wz.30 version found its way into German and Soviet hands after the country's conquest and partition in 1939, Germany calling the type the 7.9mm s MG 249(p) and the Soviets shortening the Polish designation to CKM wz.30. Up to 1939 the FN company in Belgium produced the weapon under licence for export, mainly to South American nations. The M1917 was a fine weapon, and gave good service to its users.

SPECIFICATIONS

M1917

Type:
medium water-cooled machine gun

Calibre:
7.62mm (0.3in)

Length:
0.981m (38.64in)

Length of barrel:
0.607m (23.9in)

Weight:
14.7kg (32.6lb) without cooling water

Muzzle velocity:
854m (2800ft) per second

Feed:
250-round fabric or metal link belt (450–600rpm)

M1919

SPECIFICATIONS

M1919

Type:
  light air-cooled machine gun

Calibre:
  7.62mm (0.3in)

Length:
  1.041m (41in)

Length of barrel:
  0.61m (24in)

Weight:
  13.95kg (31lb)

Muzzle velocity:
  854m (2800ft) per second

Feed:
  250-round fabric or metal link belt (400–500rpm)

The Machine Gun, Caliber .30in, M1919 was basically an air-cooled development of the M1917 water-cooled machine gun, and was originally designed for use in tanks that were not produced. The M1917 was therefore developed as the M1919A1 for the infantry, the M1919A2 for the cavalry and the M1919A3, but none of these was made in large numbers and there followed the M1919A4 (specification at left) for service either in armoured vehicles or on a tripod mounting.

This was one of the definitive machine guns of World War II, in whose course almost 440,000 were manufactured for service with most Allied nations. The M1919A5 was a development of the M1919A4 specifically for use in armoured vehicles, and finally there arrived the M1919A6 infantry squad weapon that was the M1919A4 with a bipod, butt and carrying handle. A weapon of which almost 43,500 examples were manufactured, the M1919A6 was as successful in service as the M1919A4, and like this weapon became very popular despite the fact that it was slightly on the heavy side by the standards of other light machine guns. It is worth noting that the M1919 was also the basis for the M2 series of medium machine guns that were the core of US warplanes' armament in the period before and into World War II.

M2

The first machine gun designed by John Browning in 12.7mm (0.5in) calibre was the Model 1921 that was based on a scaled-up version of the action of the 7.62mm (0.3in) M1917 gun to fire a 0.5in round derived from the 13mm (0.512in) round of the Germans' T-Gewehr anti-tank rifle. The Model 1921 and improved Model 1921A were subsequently developed into the Machine Gun, Caliber .50in, M2 that was itself the starting point for a family of heavy machine guns all using the same mechanism and differing only in their types of barrel and installation. One of the first variants was the M2, which was a water-cooled weapon used in the anti-aircraft role (examples of this variant are shown in the photograph) and installed on many of the US Navy's ships. Another variant was the M2HB (heavy barrel) air-cooled weapon (specification at right) intended mainly for use in fixed installations, armoured vehicles and aircraft. There was also a downgraded variant of the M2 which had a lighter barrel and was therefore not usable for the sustained-fire role.

The M2 series was manufactured in very large numbers (greater than that of any other American machine gun), and in 1944 a development of the M2 with a higher rate of fire was introduced as the M3 for aircraft installations.

SPECIFICATIONS

M2

Type:
heavy air-cooled machine gun

Calibre:
12.7mm (0.5in)

Length:
1.65m (65.1in)

Length of barrel:
1.14m (45in)

Weight:
38.1kg (84lb) gun; 19.95kg (44lb) tripod mounting

Muzzle velocity:
866m (2840ft) per second

Feed:
110-round metal link belt (450–550rpm)

NAGANT 1895

SPECIFICATIONS

NAGANT 1895

Type:
  revolver pistol

Calibre:
  7.62mm (0.3in)

Length:
  0.23m (9.055in)

Length of barrel:
  0.11m (4.35in)

Weight:
  0.795kg (1.75lb)

Muzzle velocity:
  272m (892ft) per second

Feed:
  7-round cylinder

The Belgian-designed Nagant revolver of 1895 was the standard Russian Army pistol in both world wars, but initially entered production in Liège before a Russian production facility was launched in Tula after the weapon's adoption for Russian service.

The Nagant revolver had several unusual features including the efforts made to create a gas-tight seal between the revolving cylinder and the barrel: the special round fired by the revolver had the tip of the bullet flush with the front of the cartridge, and the cylinder was also shifted forward against the rear of the barrel as the hammer was cocked.

There were single- and double-action variants of the revolver, these being issued to enlisted men and officers respectively. In overall terms the revolver was sturdy in its design and construction, the Germans using captured examples with the designation Revolver 612(r) to complement the R 612(p) weapons taken from the Poles in 1939. Greece also used the Nagant revolver in two forms, the Model 1895 being complemented by the Model 1912. Overall, though the design was sound, the weapon was an unremarkable piece, although for service on the Eastern Front, which was subject to wide temperature extremes and terrain variations, it performed well enough.

TULA-TOKAREVA 30-33

The two versions of the Soviets' Pistolet Tula-Tokareva (pistol made at Tula and designed by Fedor V. Tokarev), namely the obrazets 1930 and obrazets 1933, were better known as the TT30 and TT33 respectively. Both were based on the well-established Browning pistol design, from which they differed mainly in the use of a "packaged" sear and hammer assembly installed and removed as a unit, and the TT33 differed from the TT30 baseline model mainly in features designed to facilitate and therefore cheapen and speed production.

The TT33 was manufactured in altogether larger numbers than the TT30 in a programme that lasted until well after the end of World War II, and despite the decline in production standards as this war took its toll on the USSR's industrial capabilities, the TT33 remained an effective sidearm that was sturdy and reliable.

In the period of their great advances into the USSR during the second half of 1941, the Germans seized sufficient examples of the TT30 and TT33 to undertake a relatively wide distribution of what was now the Pistole 615(r) to the army and army force. As with most Red Army small arms, the Tula was easy to strip and re-assemble in the field, which meant maintenance was relatively easy and straightforward. However, as mentioned above, parts quality was variable.

SPECIFICATIONS

TULA-TOKAREVA 30-33

Type:
semi-automatic pistol

Calibre:
7.62mm (0.3in)

Length:
0.195m (7.68in)

Length of barrel:
0.116m (4.57in)

Weight:
0.854kg (1.88lb)

Muzzle velocity:
420m (1378ft) per second

Feed:
8-round detachable straight box magazine

MOSIN-NAGANT M1891

SPECIFICATIONS

MOSIN-NAGANT M1891

Type:
  bolt-action rifle

Calibre:
  7.62mm (0.3in)

Length:
  1.305m (51.37in)

Length of barrel:
  0.802m (31.2in)

Weight:
  4.37kg (9.62lb)

Muzzle velocity:
  810m (2660ft) per second

Feed:
  5-round fixed box magazine

It was in 1891 that the Imperial Russian Army standardized the Mosin-Nagant rifle that combined features created by the Belgian Nagin brothers (magazine) and the Russian Colonel N.I. Mosin (action). The Russkaya 3-linenaye vintovka obrazets 1891 was developed when a standard Russian unit of distance was the "line", almost exactly 2.54mm, so the three "lines" of the calibre were thus 7.62mm. The obrazets 1891 (see specification) was the standard Russian rifle of World War I in a form with updated sights and improved ammunition, and remained in service after the Soviet revolution right through to the USSR's involvement in World War II. Although the Germans captured large numbers of these rifles in 1941, the calibration of their sights in non-metric units meant that only a limited distribution was made of what was now known as the 7.62mm Gewehr 252(r). A variant for cavalry use was also produced from 1891 with a shortened barrel. Other countries who used the rifle were Yugoslavia (Puska 7.62mm M91R bought from the USSR), Poland (karabin wz.91/98/25 produced locally with a shorter barrel and some Mauser-type furniture and fittings) and Finland (Russian actions combined with otherwise indigenous manufacture to create the m/27 shorter than the obrazets 1891, and m/28, the m/28/30).

MOSIN-NAGANT M91/30

The vintovka obrazets 1891/30 was a shortened development of the obrazets 1891 rifle with more modern sights and changes to facilitate mass production. The obrazets 1891/30 was the Soviet Army's standard rifle through the "Great Patriotic War" with Germany between 1941 and 1945, and was also produced in a sniper model that could be fitted with either the PU x3.5 or PE x4 telescopic sight, and had a turned-down bolt handle to avoid hitting the telescopic sight.

These weapons entered service in 1937, and became a major component in the Soviets' World War II propaganda extolling the courage and skill of snipers. Oddly enough for a service rifle, the obrazets 1891/30 could also be fitted with a silencer, but a more natural adjunct was the Granatomet Djakonowa obrazets 1930, which was a cup-type grenade launcher for attachment to the muzzle; this was used in conjunction with a special sight and a bipod attached under the forestock.

The Germans captured very large numbers of obrazets 1891/30 rifles in 1941 and 1942, and these were issued with the revised designation 7.62mm Gewehr 254(r) to German second-line forces as well as anti-Soviet units raised from prisoners of war.

SPECIFICATIONS

MOSIN-NAGANT M1891/30

Type:
bolt-action rifle

Calibre:
7.62mm (0.3in)

Length:
1.232m (48.5in)

Length of barrel:
0.729m (28.7in)

Weight:
4kg (8.8lb)

Muzzle velocity:
810m (2657ft) per second

Feed:
5-round fixed box magazine

MOSIN-NAGANT M1938

SPECIFICATIONS

MOSIN-NAGANT M1938

Type:
 bolt-action carbine

Calibre:
 7.62mm (0.3in)

Length:
 1.016m (40in)

Length of barrel:
 0.508m (20in)

Weight:
 3.47kg (7.6lb)

Muzzle velocity:
 765m (2510ft) per second

Feed:
 5-round fixed box magazine

As was inevitable at a time when horsed cavalry was considered as important as, if not actually more significant than, the infantry, the Russians needed a shorter version of its long infantry rifle that could be carried in a cavalryman's saddle holster and also serve as the personal weapon of troops such as gunners. The first genuine carbine version of the Mosin-Nagant rifle was the karabin obrazets 1910. Only limited production was undertaken of this weapon, which was in essence a truncated version of the obrazets 1891 rifle and could not be fitted with a bayonet.

Cavalry continued to be important to the Soviets in the period before World War II, and this led to the development of the karabin obrazets 1938 (see specification), which was basically the karabin obrazets 1910 upgraded to vintovka 1891/30 standard, and the Germans used captured examples with the designation Karabiner 453(r).

The final version was the karabin obrazets 1944, which was in fact the last Mosin-Nagant weapon to enter production. This differed from the obrazets 1938 weapon only in its permanently attached folding bayonet. The German Army used limited numbers of captured weapons on the Eastern Front with the designation Karabiner 457(r).

SIMONOV 1936

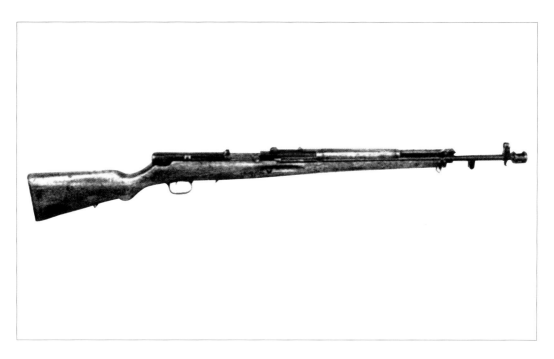

The first semi-automatic rifle placed in service by the Soviet Army, the Avtomaticheskaya vintovka Simonova obrazets 1936 (AVS or AVS36) was designed from the early 1930s by S.G. Simonov. Despite a lengthy period of intensive development, however, this gas-operated self-loading weapon was not successful. Perhaps to ensure that the weapon, which was comparatively expensive to produce, would offer capability in more than one role, it was fitted with a selector that permitted the firer to deliver single-shot or automatic fire. This latter suggests that a light machine gun capability in the rifle section support role was envisaged, but the high level of muzzle blast and flash made this impossible and also required the installation of combined compensator and muzzle brake that was efficient in neither task. Another difficulty was that the design of the action meant that the bolt handle travelled to and fro in an open slot: this was dangerous to the firer and also allowed dirt to enter and jam the operating mechanism. The AVS was accordingly pulled out of service from 1938, although there were still examples in service (mainly with second-line forces and, in a form with a telescopic sight, snipers) at the time of Germany's 1941 invasion. The Germans used small numbers with the designation Selbstladegewehr 257(r).

SPECIFICATIONS

SIMONOV 1936

Type:
semi-automatic rifle

Calibre:
7.62mm (0.3in)

Length:
12.34m (48.6in)

Length of barrel:
0.614m (24.16in)

Weight:
4.05kg (8.93lb) without the magazine

Muzzle velocity:
840m (2756ft) per second

Feed:
15-round detachable straight box magazine

TOKAREV M1940

SPECIFICATIONS

TOKAREV M1940

Type:
  semi-automatic rifle

Calibre:
  7.62mm (0.3in)

Length:
  1.222m (48.1in)

Length of barrel:
  0.625m (24.6in)

Weight:
  3.89kg (8.56lb)

Muzzle velocity:
  830m (2723ft) per second

Feed:
  10-round detachable straight box magazine

Realizing that the operating system of the SVT38 was too flimsy for service use but technically sound, the Soviet authorities ordered further development to create the Samozariadniya vintovka Tokareva obrazets 1940 (SVT40) (specifications for this weapon are given in the table at left). This was a beefed-up weapon that possessed adequate strength, but was still unpopular with the troops in the field for its strong recoil. Examples selected for their accuracy were revised to carry a telescopic sight for use in the sniping role.

Two other variants were a shortened carbine model, of which small numbers were produced either as conversions of existing rifles or as new-production weapons, and a selective-fire model capable of being used in the rifle section support role. This latter was the Avtomaticheskaya vintovka Tokareva obrazets 1940 (AVT40) with a selector allowing fully automatic fire. Again only modest numbers were made, but the Germans were impressed with the type, copying the Tokarev action for use in their own Gewehr 43, and using captured SVT40 weapons with the designation Selbstladegewehr 259(r) and, in the case of those fitted with a telescopic sight, Sl Gew Zf260(r). The Tokarev was, like most Soviet weapons, a sturdy design that could withstand a lot of punishment.

PPD34/38

Designed by Vasili A. Degtyarev for service from 1934, the Pistolet-Pulemet Degtyareva obrazets 1934 and improved PPD obrazets 1934/38 submachine guns derived some of their features from a pair of foreign weapons, the Finnish m/1931 and the German MP 28/II. The first model drew its ammunition from a 73-round drum magazine but the second model used a 71-round drum magazine copied from that of the Finnish weapon. The final model, based on the second, had a simplified barrel jacket characterized by three sets of larger slots in place of the earlier models' eight sets of smaller slots.

It is believed that it was 1940 when production of this pioneering Soviet weapon ended at the two factories tasked with its manufacture. The weapon was conventional in its blowback operation, and the only notable feature of its construction was the chromed interior of the barrel (to reduce wear and thus extend life), which became standard on Soviet submachine guns. In 1941 and 1942 the Germans captured large numbers of PPD submachine guns, which they placed in service with the designation Maschinenpistole 716(r) firing either captured Soviet ammunition or the Mauser 7.63mm pistol round that was dimensionally identical to the Soviet type.

SPECIFICATIONS

PPD34/38

Type:
  submachine gun

Calibre:
  7.62mm (0.3in)

Length:
  0.777m (30.6in)

Length of barrel:
  0.273m (10.75in)

Weight:
  3.74kg (8.25lb)

Muzzle velocity:
  490m (1608ft) per second

Feed:
  71-round drum or 25-round box magazine (800rpm)

PPD38/40

SPECIFICATIONS

PPD38/40

Type:
  submachine gun

Calibre:
  7.62mm (0.3in)

Length:
  0.787m (31in)

Length of barrel:
  0.26m (10.5in)

Weight:
  3.63kg (8lb)

Muzzle velocity:
  490m (1608ft) per second

Feed:
  71-round detachable drum magazine (800rpm)

The Pistolet-Pulemet Degtyareva obrazets 1940 (PPD40) was a development of the original PPD designed to facilitate production, and was introduced in time for service in the later stages of the Russo-Finnish "Winter War" of 1939–40.

Despite the fact that it had been re-designed to speed production and, wherever possible, reduce manufacturing costs, the PPD38/40 was still produced from high-quality materials in the fashion typical of peace- rather than wartime planning, and as a result was taken out of production in 1941 after the German invasion of the Soviet Union.

Although the PPD38/40 resembled its predecessor in many respects, and indeed benefited from the interchangeability of many of its components, it had a different bolt and drew its ammunition from a new type of 71-round drum magazine: this latter fitted into a recess in the underside of the receiver rather than having a tongue that was pushed up into a hole in the receiver as in the earlier weapon. The weapon was effective and reliable, and as a result the Germans used all such weapons that they captured with the revised designation Maschinenpistole 715(r). Both sides continued to use this weapon on the Eastern Front until the end of the war.

PPSH41

The German invasion in the second half of 1941 cost the USSR not only vast amounts of territory, people and matériel, but also much of the country's industrial capability. The urgent need for rearmament had to be undertaken in this context, and one of the answers was a submachine gun that could be produced quickly and cheaply. This weapon emerged as the Pistolet-Pulemet Shpagina obrazets 1941 (PPSh41) designed by Georgi S. Shpagin. The weapon entered service in 1942, and was so easy to manufacture that more than five million had been delivered by the end of World War II in 1945.

The PPSh41 was simple in concept and basic design, which meant that production could be undertaken with only the most limited requirement for machining. While its finish was generally poor, with the exception of the chromed interior of the barrel, the weapon was effective and thoroughly reliable under the many types of difficult operating conditions typical of the titanic war on the Eastern Front.

Complete battalions were sometimes equipped with the PPSh41, and the weapon so impressed the Germans that they used captured weapons, revised to 9mm Parabellum calibre and a housing to accept the magazine of the MP 40, with the designation 9mm Maschinenpistole 717(r).

SPECIFICATIONS

PPSH41

Type:
  submachine gun

Calibre:
  7.62mm (0.3in)

Length:
  0.840m (33.1in)

Length of barrel:
  0.269m (10.6in)

Weight:
  3.5kg (7.7lb)

Muzzle velocity:
  490m (1608ft) per second

Feed:
  35-round box magazine or 71-drum (900–1000rpm)

PPS43

SPECIFICATIONS

PPS43

Type:
submachine gun

Calibre:
7.62mm (0.3in)

Length:
0.907m (35.7in) extended; 0.641m (25.25in) folded

Length of barrel:
0.273m (10.75in)

Weight:
3.33kg (7.34lb)

Muzzle velocity:
490m (1608ft) per second

Feed:
35-round detachable box magazine (700rpm)

The submachine gun generally known as the PPS42 (Pistolet-Pulemet Sudareva obrazets 1942) was developed and first produced under the most adverse of conditions, namely the German siege of Leningrad, which lasted from the autumn of September 1941 until early 1944. To provide the forces holding the city with an effective close-range weapon that could be manufactured inside the defensive perimeter, A. I. Sudarev designed a submachine gun assembled almost completely from of spit-welded, pinned or riveted steel stampings with wood or plastic for the pistol grips only and a folding metal butt instead of the otherwise standard wooden butt.

So successful was the PPS42 (specifications given in the table at left) that the basic type was kept in production, after the lifting of Leningrad's siege, as the improved PPS43 that was nevertheless still more simple to manufacture than the PPS42: the metal stock was shortened, the safety mechanism and magazine housing were improved, and hard rubber pistol grips were introduced for ease of use.

More than one million PPS43 weapons were made, and the Germans used captured examples with the designation Maschinenpistole 709(r). Finland also produced an m/1944 in 9mm Parabellum calibre. This was one of the great weapons of the Eastern Front.

PM1910

Many types of machine gun have been based on the Maxim gun, but the heaviest and longest-lived of these is surely the Russian Pulemet Maksima obrazets 1905 (PM1905) and its successors. This was based on an entirely unchanged Maxim operating system, and had a bronze water-cooling jacket that was changed to steel in 1910 to create the PM1910.

Production of the PM1910 lasted to 1943 in a huge stream of weapons whose last examples were virtually indistinguishable from the first. The weapon was immensely strongly built and could take in its stride rough usage and all the adverse effects of terrain and weather. The few changes introduced over the gun's production life included a filler cap, derived from a tractor radiator cap, on top of the water jacket, but these were very minor add-ons.

The gun could be installed on many types of mounting, of which the most common was the Sokolov, in essence a small artillery carriage with a pair of steel wheels, a traversing turntable and a hand-towing trail. For the antiaircraft role the PM1910 was mounted on a special tripod. The PM1910 was used right through World War II, and the Germans operated captured examples with the designation schwere Maschinengewehr 216(r), generally in fixed defences.

SPECIFICATIONS

PM1910

Type:
heavy water-cooled machine gun

Calibre:
7.62mm (0.3in)

Length:
1.107m (43.6in)

Length of barrel:
0.72m (28.4in)

Weight:
23.8 kg (52.5 in) gun; 45.2kg (99.7lb) with shield

Muzzle velocity:
865m (2838ft) per second

Feed:
250-round fabric belt (520–600rpm)

DP

SPECIFICATIONS

DP

Type:
light air-cooled machine gun

Calibre:
7.62mm (0.3in)

Length:
1.265m (49.8in)

Length of barrel:
0.605m (23.8in)

Weight:
12.2kg (26.8lb)

Muzzle velocity:
845m (2772ft) per second

Feed:
47-round detachable drum magazine (520–580rpm)

The Pulemet Degtyareva Pekhotnii (DP) light machine gun was the first machine gun of wholly Russian design to enter service. Designed in the early 1920s by Vasili A. Degtyarev, the first model was trialled as the DP1926 in competition with two modified light Maxim guns and, with a certain number of modifications, was taken into service as the DP1928, generally shortened to DP, and immediately revealed itself to be a superb weapon characterized by light weight and a simple mechanism that was nonetheless strong and reliable. The gas-operated mechanism contained a mere six moving parts, and this helped to ensure that the DP remained serviceable under the most adverse geographic and climatic extremes.

The Soviets employed the DP in very large numbers right through their involvement in World War II, and the Germans used captured weapon with the designation 7.62mm leichte Maschinengewehr 120(r). The DP's only real failing was the tendency of the main spring to become hot during protracted firing and lose its strength, resulting in jams. This was remedied in the Pulemet Degtyareva Pekhotnii Modifikatsionii (DPM or DPM44) (see specification at left), which also had a pistol grip behind the trigger, a strengthened and improved bipod, and no grip safety.

DSHK38

It was in 1939 that the Krasnoi Pulemet Degtyereva-Shpagina obrazets 1938 (DShK38) entered Soviet service as a heavy machine gun in 12.7mm calibre based – unlike the tactically similar Browning M2 series with its recoil operation – on the Degtyarev type of gas-operated mechanism and a feed arrangement created by another celebrated Soviet small arms engineer, Georgi Shpagin.

The DShK38 was an extremely capable and successful weapon whose applications were gradually extended to include installation as the secondary armament of Soviet tanks, as well as on armoured trains and fast attack craft of various types. It was in the ground role that the DShK38 played its most important part in the Soviet victory over the Germans, though, and in this application the weapon was generally installed on the obrazets 1938 mounting adapted from that of another heavy machine gun, the 7.62mm PM1910. There was also a special anti-aircraft mounting to provide the gun with large angles of elevation and traverse. There were also twin and quadruple anti-aircraft mountings of the DShK38. This weapon was still being used by Russian and Afghan forces in Afghanistan during the Soviet occupation in the 1980s. It was an overall excellent and robust weapon.

SPECIFICATIONS

DSHK38

Type:
heavy air-cooled machine gun

Calibre:
12.7mm (0.5in)

Length:
1.602m (62.3in)

Length of barrel:
1.002m (39.4in)

Weight:
33.3kg (73.5lb)

Muzzle velocity:
845m (2772ft) per second

Feed:
250-round belt (550–600rpm)

AUG-A1

The AUG (*Armee Universal Gewehr* – Universal Army Rifle) was developed by the Austrian company Steyr-Mannlicher AG in the 1970s and its production began in 1978. It was almost immediately adopted by the Austrian Army as the Stg 77 (*Sturmgewehr* 77 – Assault Rifle, Model 1977). It later entered service with the armies of Australia, New Zealand, Oman, Malaysia, Saudi Arabia and Ireland, as well as with the US Coast Guard.

From the start the AUG was designed with versatility in mind: quick-interchange barrels (they can be removed and re-installed within seconds, even when hot, as a front grip is used as a barrel-replacement handle) of different lengths, and an ambidextrous fire capability. The AUG features an aluminium alloy receiver and polymer stock, bullpup layout, and conventional gas-powered action with rotating bolt. The bolt carrier itself rides on two guide rods and thus does not come into contact with the receiver. The left rod interoperates with the charging handle, while the right rod also acts as a gas piston. The hammer group is located in the butt-stock and is made almost entirely from polymer, including the hammer itself. The translucent magazine allows the user to see how much ammunition has been expended in action. Despite its looks the AUG is very strong, and in tests has worked after having been driven over by an army truck.

SPECIFICATIONS

Manufacturer:	*Steyr-Mannlicher AG*
Type:	*assault rifle*
Calibre:	*5.56mm*
Cartridge:	*5.56mm x 45mm M193 or NATO*
Length:	*790mm (31.1in)*
Length of barrel:	*508mm (20in)*
Number of grooves:	*6*
Weight:	*3.6kg (7.92lb)*
Cyclic rate of fire:	*650rpm*
Practical rate of fire:	*150rpm*
Operation:	*gas*
Magazine capacity:	*30*
Fire mode:	*semi-, full-auto*
Muzzle velocity:	*970mps (3182lps)*
Maximum range:	*1000m (3280ft)*
Effective range:	*400m (1312ft)*
Entered service:	*1978*

AUG-A2

The Steyr AUG-A2 is an improved version of the standard AUG assault rifle. It is a gas-operated, semi- and full-automatic assault rifle with a locked bolt action, quick-change barrel and integrated optical sight. The main difference between the A1 and A2 is the housing group: the A2 housing has a removable standard optical sight, which allows quick attachment of the Military Standard 1913 rail.

The A2 can be equipped with either a 407mm (16in) or 508mm (20in) barrel, each one having a gas regulator and a swing/pivot-type barrel grip. This gun's gas regulator has two action settings for firing, in order to ensure proper function under all environmental conditions. The "pull-through" trigger system fires semi-automatic when pulled halfway to a clearly felt point, and fires full-automatic when pulled fully back.

The bolt is of the fixed locking-turn variety, with eight locking lugs. The rifle can easily be changed from right to left-hand ejection by flipping the ejection port lid to the other side and installing a left-hand bolt (no tools are needed for this procedure). The AUG's modular concept allows for field stripping into the main groups within a few seconds. The casing can be olive drab, sand or black depending on user requirements.

SPECIFICATIONS

Manufacturer:	*Steyr-Mannlicher AG*
Type:	*assault rifle*
Calibre:	*5.56mm*
Cartridge:	*5.56mm x 45mm M193 or NATO*
Length:	*690–790mm (27.16–31.1in)*
Length of barrel:	*407–508mm (16–20in)*
Number of grooves:	*6*
Weight:	*3.6kg (7.92lb)*
Cyclic rate of fire:	*650rpm*
Practical rate of fire:	*150rpm*
Operation:	*gas*
Magazine capacity:	*30*
Fire mode:	*semi-, full-auto*
Muzzle velocity:	*970mps (3182lps)*
Maximum range:	*1000m (3280ft)*
Effective range:	*400m (1312ft)*
Entered service:	*1981*

AUG HBAR

The AUG assault rifle lends itself to a number of variants, including the HBAR (Heavy Barrelled Automatic Rifle), which has a 621mm (24in) barrel to become a light machine gun. With the strong Steyr bipod, the HBAR can also function as a sniping weapon. Well-designed, sturdy and mounted close to the muzzle, the bipod's legs elevate and lock like the venerable Mk I Bren bipod of World War II. When this barrel is used in the mode of a light support weapon, an open-bolt firing kit can be fitted to avoid "cook-offs" during sustained fire. Two large ports on each side and three small holes in front effectively control muzzle climb.

One thing that the HBAR lacks is a bayonet. There is a reason for this: the Austrian Army believes bayonets are archaic and inhumane, thus Austrian barrels don't have studs for bayonets. However, multi-purpose and lightweight bayonets are available to other users (a stud clamps on to mount them) should they request them.

The furniture is made from all high-impact plastic, which comes in military green, black and desert tan (the latter for Saudi use). Because the HBAR is a light support weapon, a 42-round magazine can be fitted in addition to the standard 30-round model. The longer barrel gives the HBAR a longer range, though weight increase is minimal.

SPECIFICATIONS

Manufacturer:	Steyr-Mannlicher AG
Type:	light support weapon
Calibre:	5.56mm
Cartridge:	5.56mm x 45mm M193 or NATO
Length:	900mm (35.43in)
Length of barrel:	621mm (24.45in)
Number of grooves:	6
Weight:	4.9kg (10.78lb)
Cyclic rate of fire:	680rpm
Practical rate of fire:	150rpm
Operation:	gas
Magazine capacity:	30 or 42 rounds
Fire mode:	semi-, full-auto
Muzzle velocity:	1000mps (320fps)
Maximum range:	1500m (4921ft)
Effective range:	500m (1640ft)
Entered service:	1980

AUG PARA

Taking advantage of the AUG's modularity, Steyr engineers have designed a kit which allows the user to convert an AUG into a 9mm carbine without the use of tools. The kit consists of a barrel group, bolt group, 25- or 32-round magazine and magazine adaptor. The carrier assembly differs from the .223 version in that it does not require the use of a rotating bolt. Also, the bolt allows only for right-handed ejection, so the stock's port cover must be situated accordingly on the left side. The magazine adaptor emulates the top of a .223 magazine and remains fixed to the stock during magazine changes. It contains its own bolt hold-open actuator, which is triggered by the 9mm magazine follower. Because it utilizes the blowback principle, there is no gas port or piston in the 406mm (16in) barrel assembly. A 9mm AUG measures 665mm (26in) in length and is marginally shorter than a Heckler & Koch MP5A2 submachine gun, which uses a 225mm (8.85in) barrel.

As the AUG is a system, four different barrels fit any receiver in a matter of seconds. This makes four different weapons. All barrels are constructed of high-quality steel by the cold-hammer forging process developed by GFM of Steyr, Austria, and bores and chambers are chrome-plated to increase barrel life. Barrels have six grooves with a right-hand twist of one turn in 229mm (9in).

SPECIFICATIONS

Manufacturer:	*Steyr-Mannlicher AG*
Type:	*assault rifle*
Calibre:	*9mm*
Cartridge:	*9mm Parabellum*
Length:	*665mm (26in)*
Length of barrel:	*406mm (16in)*
Number of grooves:	6
Weight:	*3.3kg (7.26lb)*
Cyclic rate of fire:	*700rpm*
Practical rate of fire:	*150rpm*
Operation:	*blowback*
Magazine capacity:	*25 or 32*
Fire mode:	*semi-, full-auto*
Muzzle velocity:	*400mps (1312fps)*
Maximum range:	*400m (1312ft)*
Effective range:	*50m (164ft)*
Entered service:	*1986*

MPI 69

This submachine gun has a receiver made from bent and welded sheet steel that is carried in the frame unit. The magazine feeds in through the pistol grip, and the bolt is of the "wrap-around" or "telescoped" type: the actual bolt face is well back within the bolt and much of the bolt mass is in front of the breech at the moment of firing. This system allows the maximum mass for the minimum bolt stroke and assists in producing a compact weapon. Cocking is performed by pulling on the carry sling, which is attached at the forward end to the cocking knob (a bracket welded into the top of the receiver ensures that the cocking action can only be performed when the sling is held at right angles to the receiver, on the left-hand side). The normal pull from the top of the weapon, as when slinging it over the shoulder, cannot move the cocking piece.

There is a safety catch in the form of a cross-bolt above the trigger which locks the trigger when set to safe. It is a three-position bolt; when pushed across to the right so that a white "S" protrudes, it is safe; when pushed across to the left so that a red "F" protrudes, it is set for automatic fire. There is also a halfway position in which single shots are possible.

Overall the MPi 69 is easy to strip and re-assemble, and is a well-designed and robust submachine gun.

SPECIFICATIONS

Manufacturer:	*Steyr-Mannlicher AG*
Type:	*submachine gun*
Calibre:	*9mm*
Cartridge:	*9mm Parabellum*
Length:	*465–670mm (18.31–26.38in)*
Length of barrel:	*260mm (10.24in)*
Number of grooves:	6
Weight:	*3.13kg (6.88lb)*
Cyclic rate of fire:	*550rpm*
Practical rate of fire:	*200rpm*
Operation:	*blowback*
Magazine capacity:	*25 or 32*
Fire mode:	*semi-, full-auto*
Muzzle velocity:	*381mps (1250fps)*
Maximum range:	*100m (328ft)*
Effective range:	*50m (164ft)*
Entered service:	*1969*

SSG PIV

The Steyr SSG 69 was adopted by the Austrian Army in 1969. It is a bolt-action, rotating bolt, magazine-fed rifle which is an excellent weapon and has been produced in a number of variants, including models with heavy barrels, short barrels and silencers. The barrel is cold-hammer forged and the standard feeding device is a detachable Steyr-type rotary magazine.

The Steyr SSG is offered to military, police and civilian shooters in four different models: the SSG PI, SSG PII, SSG PIIK and the SSG PIV. The SSG PI was originally developed as a counter-sniper rifle, and was the first such weapon to be equipped with a synthetic stock. It has a 660mm (26in) barrel and is equipped with iron sights, as well as standard NATO-specified dovetails for a telescopic sight. The SSG PII is built for police use as a tactical or sniper rifle. It has a heavy barrel, lacks iron sights and has an oversized bolt handle for quick follow-up shots (essential for hostage-rescue operations when multiple targets often present themselves). The SSG PIIK differs from the SSG PII only by a shorter barrel and is for use in crowded urban situations – despite the shorter barrel accuracy is not degraded up to a range of 500m (1640ft). The SSG PIV has a 406mm (16in) barrel with detachable flash hider, which can easily be changed to a sound suppressor (silencer).

SPECIFICATIONS

Manufacturer:	*Steyr-Mannlicher AG*
Type:	*sniper rifle*
Calibre:	*7.62mm*
Cartridge:	*7.62 x 51mm NATO*
Length:	*896mm (35.27in)*
Length of barrel:	*406mm (16in)*
Number of grooves:	*4*
Weight:	*3.9kg (8.58lb)*
Cyclic rate of fire:	*n/a*
Practical rate of fire:	*5rpm*
Operation:	*bolt*
Magazine capacity:	*5*
Fire mode:	*single shot*
Muzzle velocity:	*860mps (2822fps)*
Maximum range:	*2000m (6561ft)*
Effective range:	*1000m (3280ft)*
Entered service:	*1969*

F2000

The F2000 allows accessories to be added while respecting the ergonomics, balance and smooth lines of an assault rifle. Space is provided inside the weapon for a centralized power pack, and it can be used by left-handed firers without modifications thanks to the forward ejection. The bullpup design gives a very compact rifle with a full-length barrel. Light, with excellent balance, and with a smooth outer shape, the F2000 is easy and comfortable to carry. The firing selector and magazine catch are easily accessed.

For a grenade to be effective it must hit within a few metres of the target. In operational conditions this is very difficult. Grenades are heavy projectiles launched at low velocity, so they normally have a high, curved trajectory. Few grenades land close to their target, and initial volleys are almost always well off target.

The F2000's fire control system provides a means of quickly and accurately aiming the grenade launcher, which greatly increases its effect. It ensures a high probability of achieving an effective hit with a minimum number of grenades. A laser rangefinder first determines the range to the target and then a ballistic computer, programmed with three firing tables, automatically calculates the launch angle. An infra-red laser pointer allows aiming at night.

SPECIFICATIONS

Manufacturer:	FN Herstal
Type:	integrated weapon system
Calibre:	5.56mm
Cartridge:	5.56 x 45mm NATO
Length:	694mm (27.32in)
Length of barrel:	400mm (15.74in)
Number of grooves:	unknown
Weight:	3.6kg (7.92lb)
Cyclic rate of fire:	850rpm
Practical rate of fire:	unknown
Operation:	gas
Magazine capacity:	30
Fire mode:	unknown
Muzzle velocity:	900mps (2952fps)
Maximum range:	unknown
Effective range:	unknown
Entered service:	not yet in service

FN FAL

The FAL is a gas-operated rifle and fires from the closed-bolt position in both the semi- and full-auto modes. It has an operator-adjustable gas regulator which works on the "exhaust" principle. Under ideal conditions the major portion of the gas is passed through the regulator and out into the air, which helps to reduce recoil.

The trigger mechanism of the FAL is well designed and has been copied around the world. It incorporates both the usual sear, which is attached to the trigger by a pin, and an "automatic safety sear" which is in front of the hammer and must be depressed for the hammer to rotate.

Originally the FAL was designed to fire the 7.92mm round, but once NATO opted for the 7.62mm round the rifle was redesigned to accept this calibre. The FAL was an instant success and though not particularly compact or light, it is very accurate and robust. The FAL always fires from a closed bolt, and most models can fire both semi- or full-automatic. That said, the 7.62mm round is really too powerful for controllable, hand-held automatic fire. One valuable feature is the adjustable gas plug that controls the amount of gas diverted against the piston. If the rifle becomes fouled in dusty conditions, for example, the extra gas pressure will overcome any tendency to jam. The FAL is undoubtedly one of the greatest assault rifles ever built.

SPECIFICATIONS

Manufacturer:	FN Herstal
Type:	assault rifle
Calibre:	7.62mm
Cartridge:	7.62 x 51mm NATO
Length:	1090mm (42.9in)
Length of barrel:	533mm (20.98in)
Number of grooves:	4
Weight:	4.25kg (9.35lb)
Cyclic rate of fire:	650–700rpm
Practical rate of fire:	200rpm
Operation:	gas
Magazine capacity:	20
Fire mode:	semi-, full-auto
Muzzle velocity:	840mps (2756fps)
Maximum range:	1200m (3937ft)
Effective range:	550m (1804ft)
Entered service:	1953

FN FNC

The gas-operated FNC rifle was a replacement for FN's CAL rifle (which was a scaled-down version of the FAL, using the same gas system and tipping bolt) and fires from a closed bolt. Mounted above the barrel, the gas cylinder has six ports 38mm (1.5in) behind the barrel's gas vent. At the end of this short stroke, all gases escape the cylinder when the piston head passes the exhaust ports. A handle welded to the rear of the gas cylinder rotates the cylinder, opening and closing a small port in the gas block. When the adjustment handle is rotated to the left, this gas block port is exposed and a small amount of the propellant gases escapes before the piston begins its rearward travel.

The FNC can fire grenades from its muzzle with blank ammunition using a sheet-metal, flip-up, combination grenade sight/gas valve called the alidade. The alidade is attached to the gas block/front sight assembly. When pivoted up to the vertical position, the alidade axis turns to close the gas vent. Then all gases propel the grenade. Using this procedure all propellant gases bypass the gas system, thus the weapon does not cycle and the bolt must be retracted manually.

The FNC has a slab-sided receiver, and a round, ribbed fore-end with flutes. It is a selective-fire weapon which also has a three-round burst facility.

SPECIFICATIONS

Manufacturer:	FN Herstal
Type:	assault rifle
Calibre:	5.56mm
Cartridge:	5.56 x 45mm NATO
Length:	756–1000mm (29.76in–39.37in)
Length of barrel:	449mm (17.68in)
Number of grooves:	6
Weight:	3.8kg (8.36lb)
Cyclic rate of fire:	650–700rpm
Practical rate of fire:	200rpm
Operation:	gas
Magazine capacity:	30
Fire mode:	semi-, full-auto, three-round burst
Muzzle velocity:	965mps (3166fps)
Maximum range:	600m (1968ft)
Effective range:	450m (1476ft)
Entered service:	1976

FN MAG

The FN *Mitrailleuse d'Appui Général* (MAG), meaning General Purpose Machine Gun, has been adopted by more than 20 countries, including USA (under the designation M240), Great Britain (L7 GPMG), Israel, India and Sweden. All MAGs and its derivatives have quick-interchangeable barrels that can be swapped in a battlefield environment (an essential facility as machine-gun barrels overheat when subjected to intensive combat use). When mounted on a bipod the MAG is an infantry support weapon; on a heavier tripod it becomes a heavy support weapon. It can also be mounted on vehicle turrets or pintles for primary, coaxial or air-defence purposes.

The gas piston sits inside the cylinder and is connected to an extension piece and a piston post. A slot in the extension piece allows empty gases to pass through and be ejected beneath the gun. When the weapon is cocked the piston and piston port are pulled back against the return spring, pulling the bolt with them. Next they fly forward, and the bolt takes the next round from the ammunition belt. Normal sights are a leaf rear sight, which is folded upright for long ranges but laid down as a sight for short- and medium-range firing. The basic MAG has a wooden butt, smooth barrel, pistol grip and slotted flash eliminator. However, different armies have tailored the weapon to their own preferences.

SPECIFICATIONS

Manufacturer:	*FN Herstal*
Type:	*machine gun*
Calibre:	*7.62mm*
Cartridge:	*7.62 x 51mm NATO*
Length:	*1250mm (49.2in)*
Length of barrel:	*546mm (21.5in)*
Number of grooves:	*4*
Weight:	*10.15kg (22.33lb)*
Cyclic rate of fire:	*850rpm*
Practical rate of fire:	*200rpm*
Operation:	*gas*
Magazine capacity:	*metal link belt*
Fire mode:	*full-auto*
Muzzle velocity:	*853mps (2800fps)*
Maximum range:	*3000m (9842ft)*
Effective range:	*1800m (5905ft)*
Entered service:	*1955*

M240G

After extensive tests, the US Army selected the M240B 7.62mm medium machine gun produced by Fabrique Nationale as a replacement for the M60 machine gun. The M240 is a licence-produced version of the FN MAG. This is a ground-mounted variant of the original M240/M240C/M240E1 coaxial/pintle-mounted machine gun used on M2/M3 Bradley infantry fighting vehicles, the M1 Abrams main battle tank, and the US Marine Corps' Light Armored Vehicles (LAVs). While possessing many of the same basic characteristics as the M60 medium machine gun, the M240 has superior reliability and maintainability compared to the M60.

The M240D 7.62mm machine gun is a left-hand feed, gas-operated, air-cooled, fixed headspace weapon. It can be configured for two roles: aircraft and ground. In the aircraft configuration the M240D has a front and rear sight and a trigger group which accommodates the spade grip device.

The M240G version has a bipod and can also be mounted on a tripod if need be. Thus in this guise the weapon reverts back to its original ground role. There are some minor differences between the M240G and the FN MAG due to the lengthy development history, but essentially the US version has retained the reliability and robustness of its venerable Belgian parent.

SPECIFICATIONS

Manufacturer:	*FN Herstal*
Type:	*medium machine gun*
Calibre:	*7.62mm*
Cartridge:	*7.62 x 51mm NATO*
Length:	*1220mm (48.03in)*
Length of barrel:	*627mm (24.68in)*
Number of grooves:	*4*
Weight:	*11.7kg (25.74lb)*
Cyclic rate of fire:	*750rpm*
Practical rate of fire:	*200rpm*
Operation:	*gas*
Magazine capacity:	*metal link belt*
Fire mode:	*full-auto*
Muzzle velocity:	*854mps (2800fps)*
Maximum range:	*3725m (12,221ft)*
Effective range:	*1800m (5905ft)*
Entered service:	*1995*

M249

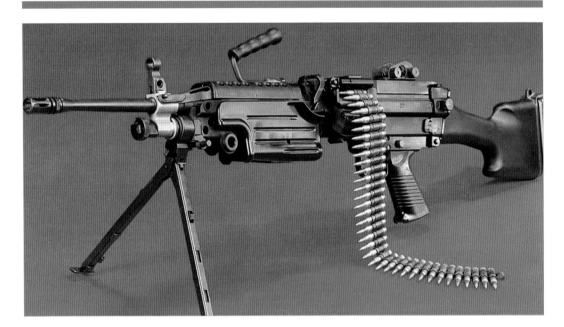

The M249 is essentially the FN Minimi Squad Automatic Weapon (SAW) with some variations to meet US military specifications. The main external differences are in the shape of the butt and fore-end/hand-guard. It has a regulator for selecting either normal (750 rounds per minute) or maximum (1000 rounds per minute) rate of fire. The M249 can be fired from the shoulder, hip or under-arm position. When employed as a machine gun it can be mounted on either a bipod or tripod, though barrels must not be interchanged with those from other M249s unless the headspace has been set for that weapon by direct support personnel.

The M249 is fed from a 200-round disintegrating belt, but is also capable of firing ammunition from standard M16 magazines inserted into a magazine well in the bottom of the SAW (a useful attribute for battlefield use when ammunition can often be in scarce supply). The M249 is used to engage dismounted infantry, crew-served weapons, anti-tank guided missile teams and thin-skinned vehicles. It has become the standard automatic rifle of the US Army infantry squad. The Belgian Minimi entered service in Europe in 1974, though the weapon entered service with the US armed forces in 1990. The specifications at right refer to the American variant of the weapon.

SPECIFICATIONS

Manufacturer:	FN Herstal
Type:	squad automatic weapon
Calibre:	5.56mm
Cartridge:	5.56 x 45mm NATO
Length:	1040mm (40.9in)
Length of barrel:	523mm (20.59in)
Number of grooves:	6
Weight:	6.85kg (15.07lb)
Cyclic rate of fire:	750–1000rpm
Practical rate of fire:	200rpm
Operation:	gas
Magazine capacity:	200-round metal link belt
Fire mode:	full-auto
Muzzle velocity:	915mps (300fps)
Maximum range:	3600m (11,811ft)
Effective range:	1000m (3280ft)
Entered service:	1990

MINIMI PARA

The Minimi Para is a compact version of the Minimi with a short barrel and a sliding butt. The Minimi's rotary gas regulator is a simplification of the FN MAG's regulator. It has two positions, normal and adverse, and is hand-adjustable. The adverse position increases the cyclic rate, though this means reliability will deteriorate due to the increased cyclic rate. The only real disadvantage to gas systems is an increase in fouling over recoil-operated weapons, a problem compounded by the current emphasis on the use of ball-type powders.

The Minimi has a chrome-lined bore and a three-second quick-change barrel, and its feed cover can be closed with the bolt in any position along the feed cam. The tubular-aluminium skeleton stock and its folding wire buttstrap are weight-saving contributions. The Minimi's push-button safety and elimination of the semi-automatic mode simplify the sear mechanism. A loaded belt indicator has been provided for night use, and the rear sight is adjustable to 1000m (3280ft). The Para version has been designed for airborne troops and is an extremely reliable weapon. The bolt is a two-piece model, with the bolt face locking into the barrel extension by means of locking lugs. A cam system on the bolt carrier causes the bolt to unlock, in a similar manner to that employed in assault rifles.

SPECIFICATIONS

Manufacturer:	FN Herstal
Type:	light machine gun
Calibre:	5.56mm
Cartridge:	5.56 x 45mm NATO
Length:	893mm (35.15in)
Length of barrel:	347mm (13.66in)
Number of grooves:	6
Weight:	7.1kg (15.62lb)
Cyclic rate of fire:	850rpm
Practical rate of fire:	200rpm
Operation:	gas
Magazine capacity:	30 or 200-round belt
Fire mode:	full-auto
Muzzle velocity:	900mps (2952fps)
Maximum range:	3600m (11,811ft)
Effective range:	1000m (3280ft)
Entered service:	1974

MINIMI SPW

The Special Purpose Weapon (SPW), which is shown above with the Para model (the SPW variant is the bottom weapon) is a special model of the M249 Minimi machine gun developed to meet a US Special Operations requirement for a lightweight variant of the M249 that would retain the intrinsic functionality and reliability of the standard model. The total reduction in weight is 1.86kg (4.1lb) – weight saving is always an imperative for special operations forces. In addition, a new lightweight barrel has been developed and the carrying handle, the magazine well and the mount lugs (for vehicle applications) have been removed. Unique to the M249 SPW are special rails to accommodate scopes, laser designators and flashlights; plus a pistol grip and a detachable bipod.

The SPW features a quick-change barrel with a fixed headspace, and an integral sight rail for an optical sight. In addition, there is a multi-rail forearm for use with additional accessories. As with the standard Minimi, the SPW version is a very reliable weapon. The SPW can also fire from M16 magazines if necessary, and when firing from a magazine the cyclic rate of fire is much faster than from a belt as the mechanism does not need to lift the weight of the 200-round belt. That said, magazine feed is really only a secondary option to be used in an emergency.

SPECIFICATIONS

Manufacturer:	*FN Herstal*
Type:	*special forces machine gun*
Calibre:	*5.56mm*
Cartridge:	*5.56 x 45mm NATO*
Length:	*775–908mm (30.5–35.75in)*
Length of barrel:	*406mm (16in)*
Number of grooves:	*6*
Weight:	*8.77kg (19.3lb)*
Cyclic rate of fire:	*850rpm*
Practical rate of fire:	*200rpm*
Operation:	*gas*
Magazine capacity:	*100- or 200-round belt*
Fire mode:	*full-auto*
Muzzle velocity:	*915mps (3000fps)*
Maximum range:	*3600m (11,811ft)*
Effective range:	*450m (1476ft)*
Entered service:	*unknown*

P90

The P90 was developed as a lightweight, small submachine gun with a large magazine capacity and low recoil. Capable of easily penetrating body armour, the P90 has been adopted by numerous government agencies all over the world.

The P90 looks very unconventional, with its top-loaded magazine, polymer construction, integral sights and an unusual stock. The weapon uses a simple blowback mechanism, and the entire barrel/bolt assembly can be lifted out of the weapon in seconds. Attached directly to this assembly is the sight, which is a non-enlarging scope and features a recticle which is highly visible in all but the very poorest of light conditions. For emergency use there are also normal sights on either side of the scope (the P90 is also fully ambidextrous).

The likelihood of dirt fouling the mechanism is minimal because when the magazine is loaded there are only two ways that dirt can enter the weapon: through the barrel or the ejection port. However, the latter is located on the underside of the weapon, which makes it unlikely that much dirt will enter via this route. Because of this, cartridges are ejected downwards (a case catcher which can hold 100 empty cases and snaps onto the ejection port is available). Other available extras are lasers, lamps and silencers.

SPECIFICATIONS

Manufacturer:	FN Herstal
Type:	personal defence weapon
Calibre:	5.7mm
Cartridge:	5.7 x 28mm
Length:	500mm (19.68in)
Length of barrel:	263mm (10.35in)
Number of grooves:	8
Weight:	2.54kg (5.58lb)
Cyclic rate of fire:	900rpm
Practical rate of fire:	200rpm
Operation:	blowback
Magazine capacity:	50
Fire mode:	semi-, full-auto
Muzzle velocity:	715mps (2345fps)
Maximum range:	400m (1312ft)
Effective range:	200m (656ft)
Entered service:	1990

TYPE 56

This is one of the many Kalashnikov clones that have been manufactured around the world, though like most Chinese copies it is inferior to the original with regard to quality of parts and engineering.

The Type 56 assault rifle was adopted by the People's Liberation Army in 1956, along with the Type 56 carbine (which is a licence-built Soviet SKS copy). The Type 56 assault rifle is, in turn, also a licensed copy of the Soviet AK-47 assault rifle, with minor modifications. The Type 56 is a gas-operated, selective-fire weapon, i.e. it fires both semi-automatic and full-automatic. The receiver is machined from steel, and the two-lugged bolt locks into the receiver walls. It has AK-47-style controls with reciprocating charging handle and massive safety/fire selector lever on the right side of the receiver. The furniture is made from wood, and the compact version with an underfolding metallic buttstock was also produced. The only visible difference between the Type 56 and the AK-47 is a permanently attached spike bayonet, which folds under the barrel when not in use. The Type 56-2 variant has a skeleton, tubular-type buttstock which folds to the right side of the receiver. The Type 56-C model appears to be a copy of the Russian AK-74 assault rifle, with plastic furniture. The side-folding butt has a cheek-piece and new muzzle compensator.

SPECIFICATIONS

Manufacturer:	*State Factories*
Type:	*assault rifle*
Calibre:	*7.62mm*
Cartridge:	*7.62 x 39mm M1943*
Length:	*869mm (34.21ft)*
Length of barrel:	*414mm (16.3in)*
Number of grooves:	*4*
Weight:	*4.3kg (9.46lb)*
Cyclic rate of fire:	*775rpm*
Practical rate of fire:	*400rpm*
Operation:	*gas*
Magazine capacity:	*30*
Fire mode:	*semi-, full-auto*
Muzzle velocity:	*710mps (2329fps)*
Maximum range:	*1000m (3280ft)*
Effective range:	*400m (1312ft)*
Entered service:	*1956*

TRG-22

The TRG range of sniper rifles was developed by the Finnish company Sako. The original models, the TRG-21 and TRG-41, were both built around Sako's TRG bolt action, with a rotating bolt having three massive lugs at the front. The same action is also used in Sako's TRG-S rifle. Other key features of the TRG sniper rifles are aluminium bedded, composite stocks with adjustable butts and cheek-pieces, heavy, match-grade barrels (which are cold-hammered with muzzle brakes) and adjustable triggers. The main difference between the TRG-21 and TRG-41 is in the ammunition used. The TRG-21 is designed to fire standard 7.62mm NATO ammunition, while the TRG-41 is designed to fire the more powerful .338 Lapua Magnum cartridge, and has a large (magnum-size) action and a longer barrel with muzzle brake. In all other respects both rifles are similar.

The TRG-22 and TRG-42 are upgraded versions of the TRG-21 and TRG-41 rifles respectively, with modified stocks and some internal changes. New stocks have slightly different contours and there are integral folding bipods at the front. Sako sniper rifles are renowned for their accuracy and strength. As a result, they are used by many European police and counter-terrorist units. They are among the élite of Europe's sniper rifles.

SPECIFICATIONS

Manufacturer:	Sako Ltd
Type:	sniper rifle
Calibre:	.308in
Cartridge:	.308 Winchester
Length:	1150mm (45.24in)
Length of barrel:	660mm (26in)
Number of grooves:	4
Weight:	4.7kg (10.25lb)
Cyclic rate of fire:	n/a
Practical rate of fire:	10rpm
Operation:	bolt
Magazine capacity:	10
Fire mode:	single shot
Muzzle velocity:	914mps (2998fps)
Maximum range:	2000m (6561ft)
Effective range:	800m (2624ft)
Entered service:	1991

TRG-42

The TRG range of sniper rifles have receivers made using the cold-hammering method, and they are stabilized with three fastening screws. The magazine is a detachable, centre-fed model which holds five rounds. The double-stage trigger pull is adjustable from 1 to 2.5kg (2 to 5lb), and is also adjustable in length and horizontal or vertical pitch. The entire trigger assembly, including the trigger guard, can be removed from the rifle without disassembling any other part of the rifle.

The safety catch, which is silent in operation, is positioned inside the trigger guard. The safety locks the trigger mechanism and locks the bolt in a closed position with the firing pin blocked. The base of the stock is made of aluminium, to which the polyurethane forestock is attached. The buttstock is also made of polyurethane and is reinforced through the use of an aluminium skeleton. Spacers allow the cheekpiece to be fully adjustable in height and infinitely adjustable in windage and pitch. As with many modern rifles, the stock is designed for both right- and left-handed shooters. The buttplate is adjustable both for distance and angle through the use of spacers, and is also infinitely adjustable in height and pitch.

Though the TRG is supplied with open sights, there is an integral dovetail on the top of the receiver for other sights.

SPECIFICATIONS

Manufacturer:	Sako Ltd
Type:	sniper rifle
Calibre:	.338in
Cartridge:	.338 Lapua Magnum
Length:	1200mm (47.24in)
Length of barrel:	690mm (27.16in)
Number of grooves:	4
Weight:	5.1kg (11.22lb)
Cyclic rate of fire:	n/a
Practical rate of fire:	10rpm
Operation:	bolt
Magazine capacity:	5
Fire mode:	single shot
Muzzle velocity:	914mps (2998fps)
Maximum range:	2000m (6561ft)
Effective range:	800m (2624ft)
Entered service:	1991

TRG-S

The TRG-S is based on a bolt-action hunting rifle with a detachable clip magazine. The single-stage trigger pull is adjustable from 1 to 2kg (2.2 to 4.4lb), and the design of the stock and pistol grip makes the rifle suitable for both right- and left-handed shooters. The straightline stock reduces recoil, which means the rifle is controllable even under arduous tactical circumstances. The stock length and heelplate angle can be easily adjusted with straight or angle spacers. The above photograph shows the TRG-S equipped with open sights with post bead, but the company also supplies this model without open sights. There are integral rails for scope mounts on top of the receiver.

The free-floating barrel is cold-hammer forged, and the company can supply stainless steel barrels if required. In addition, an optional detachable muzzle brake can be fitted, which acts as an efficient flash-hider. The TRG-S is an excellent weapon, though its three-round magazine could be considered a handicap in some tactical situations.

Sako also produce a number of accessories for their sniper rifle range. These include a suppressor (for .308in Winchester calibre), a foldable bipod, auxiliary steel peep sights for emergency use, a match sight mounting set, a night set adaptor, plus different slings, swivels, cleaning sets and transit cases.

SPECIFICATIONS

Manufacturer:	Sako Ltd
Type:	sniper rifle
Calibre:	.338in
Cartridge:	.338 Lapua Magnum
Length:	1200mm (47.24in)
Length of barrel:	660mm (26in)
Number of grooves:	4
Weight:	3.7kg (8.14lb)
Cyclic rate of fire:	n/a
Practical rate of fire:	5rpm
Operation:	bolt
Magazine capacity:	3
Fire mode:	single shot
Muzzle velocity:	914mps (2998fps)
Maximum range:	2000m (6561ft)
Effective range:	800m (2624ft)
Entered service:	1995

AA 52

The French AA 52 machine gun is more correctly termed the *Arme Automatique Transformable Modèle 1952*. It was the first machine gun to be designed and produced in France after World War II as a general purpose lightweight weapon. A later version was produced to take the NATO standard 7.62mm round, and was called the AA 7.62 F-1. This weapon has the same dimensions, but has a muzzle velocity of 830mps (2723fps) with a light barrel and 845mps (2772fps) with a heavy barrel.

The AA 52 is a belt-fed 7.5mm machine gun. A fairly mundane weapon, it is still used in the French Foreign Legion today. Because of the inaccuracy of the weapon, it can pepper-spread a large area to the front – a useful application in certain military scenarios. The weapon is simple and sturdy in construction, and stripping and assembly is not a problem. It is supplied with a bipod and sling for carrying. It has a hump-backed receiver and is belt-fed from the left. When mounted on a tripod a heavier barrel is used. The AA 52 is air-cooled and employs a two-piece bolt and fluted chamber. The heavy barrelled version can be mounted on a US M2 tripod for the sustained-fire role. With a heavier barrel the range is increased.

The specifications at right refer to the heavy barrelled version of the weapon.

SPECIFICATIONS

Manufacturer:	MAS
Type:	general purpose machine gun
Calibre:	7.5mm
Cartridge:	7.5 x 54mm French M1929
Length:	1080–1245mm (42.5–49in)
Length of barrel:	600mm (23.62in)
Number of grooves:	4
Weight:	11.37kg (25.01lb)
Cyclic rate of fire:	700rpm
Practical rate of fire:	100rpm
Operation:	delayed blowback
Magazine capacity:	disintegrating link belt
Fire mode:	full-automatic
Muzzle velocity:	823mps (2700fps)
Maximum range:	1800m (5905ft)
Effective range:	1000m (3280ft)
Entered service:	1952

FAMAS

The FAMAS was developed in the 1970s and entered service with the French Army in the early 1980s. The barrel is only fractionally shorter than that of the American M16 assault rifle, but the entire rifle is some 250mm (9.84in) shorter overall thanks to its bullpup design. It operates by a delayed blowback system based on a two-part bolt. When the trigger is pulled the case sets back against the light bolt head, and this force is transmitted to a lever which is engaged with a recess in the receiver. As the lever is turned, it has to force the heavy bolt body back at a mechanical disadvantage, so slowing the opening of the bolt.

There is the usual semi-automatic or full-automatic option, and in addition the rifle can be set to fire a three-round burst. There is a bipod for steadier shooting and a sling is also provided for off-hand firing and for use when launching grenades. The iron sights are concealed inside the channel section of the long carrying handle, beneath which is the cocking handle.

Nicknamed *Le Clairon* (The Bugle) by French troops, the FAMAS is an effective and accurate weapon. The F1 is the French military version. The G2 is the updated, NATO-standardized version and is in use outside France. Its magazine housing can accept any M16-type magazine, and the safety/selector is inside the trigger guard.

SPECIFICATIONS

Manufacturer:	MAS
Type:	assault rifle
Calibre:	5.56mm
Cartridge:	5.56 x 45mm French
Length:	757mm (29.8in)
Length of barrel:	508mm (20in)
Number of grooves:	4
Weight:	3.7kg (8.14lb)
Cyclic rate of fire:	950rpm
Practical rate of fire:	200rpm
Operation:	delayed blowback
Magazine capacity:	30
Fire mode:	semi-, full-auto, three-round burst
Muzzle velocity:	960mps (3150fps)
Maximum range:	1000m (3280ft)
Effective range:	400m (1312ft)
Entered service:	1980

FR-F2

The FR-F1 bolt-action sniper rifle was developed from the old Model 36 rifle (which was a bolt-action repeater, with the bolt locking into the receiver behind the magazine), and had a padded cheek rest and an adjustable buttstock, using a spacer system. The FR-F2 is an updated version of the FR-F1, which uses a different bipod/stock configuration and has some other general upgrades, such as a fore-end made of plastic-covered metal. The bipod is attached to a yoke around the barrel, and the barrel itself is covered with a thermal sleeve to reduce heat haze in the sight line. In addition, the bipod has been shifted rearwards to the front edge of the receiver. The bolt handle slopes forward, as with the F1. Both weapons have been around for quite some time, and while they are not at the cutting end of technology they have proven themselves reliable weapons. The FR-F2 is currently the standard-issue sniper rifle for the French military. Like Great Britain, France has opted to keep faith with bolt-action sniper rifles on the battlefield.

Iron sights are fitted as standard, but to use them the telescopic scope must be removed. Once the scope is zeroed it can be removed and replaced without further modification. The F1 model was originally in 7.5mm calibre, but later models were produced in 7.62mm chambering.

SPECIFICATIONS

Manufacturer:	MAS
Type:	sniper rifle
Calibre:	7.62mm
Cartridge:	7.62 x 51mm NATO
Length:	1138mm (44.8in)
Length of barrel:	552mm (21.73in)
Number of grooves:	4
Weight:	5.2kg (11.44lb)
Cyclic rate of fire:	n/a
Practical rate of fire:	10rpm
Operation:	bolt
Magazine capacity:	10
Fire mode:	single shot
Muzzle velocity:	852mps (2795fps)
Maximum range:	2000m (6561ft)
Effective range:	800m (2624ft)
Entered service:	1984

G3

I n 1950, the Spanish Army issued a requirement for a
modern selective-fire rifle. Development began at the
Centro de Estudios Tecnicos de Materiales Especiales, an agency
of the Spanish Government known as CETME. CETME
assembled a team of Spanish and German weapon designers.
The team included Ludwig Vorgrimmler, generally
recognized as the inventor of the delayed roller-locking
system. The breech mechanism of the StG.45 (M) was used
as the basis for the new design. Prototypes of the new rifle
were available for firing by 1952. By 1954, the 7.62mm x
51 cartridge had been standardized by the NATO alliance.
The Spanish Government approached Heckler & Koch for
adaptation of the CETME rifle in this new calibre in 1954.
After another five years of development, the West German
Army adopted the new rifle in 1959, and gave it its new
name, G3 (*Gewehr 3*).

All G3s suffer from heaviness and excessive recoil of the
7.62 x 51 cartridge in the automatic-fire mode. That said,
the stopping power of the 7.62mm round is much better
than the 5.56m bullet, and has greater range. Like all
Heckler & Koch weapons, the G3 is very reliable and very
robust. There was extensive use of steel pressings in this
selective-fire weapon. It has undergone extensive
modifications since it entered service in 1959.

SPECIFICATIONS

Manufacturer:	*Heckler & Koch*
Type:	*assault rifle*
Calibre:	*7.62mm*
Cartridge:	*7.62 x 51mm NATO*
Length:	*1021mm (40.2in)*
Length of barrel:	*450mm (17.72in)*
Number of grooves:	*4*
Weight:	*4.4kg (9.68lb)*
Cyclic rate of fire:	*550rpm*
Practical rate of fire:	*150rpm*
Operation:	*delayed blowback*
Magazine capacity:	*20*
Fire mode:	*semi-, full-auto*
Muzzle velocity:	*800mps (2625fps)*
Maximum range:	*1500m (4921ft)*
Effective range:	*550m (1804ft)*
Entered service:	*1959*

G36

The new G36/G36E is a true modular weapon system in 5.56 x 45mm calibre, which was designed for the German Army as a replacement for the G11 assault rifle. Constructed almost entirely of a tough, fibre-reinforced polymer material and using a simple, self-regulating gas system, the G36/G36E provides the user with a lightweight weapon that delivers high performance with extremely low maintenance.

The barrel of the G36/G36E can be exchanged by unit armourers to create either a rifle or a carbine, using the same common receiver. The G36 can fire frangible training ammunition without special muzzle devices. Blank and safety blank-firing devices that use conventional blank ammunition are also available as accessories.

The G36 gas system is insensitive to fouling back into the weapon's interior. This ensures reliable operation even after firing more than 15,000 rounds without cleaning. Polymer components can easily be cleaned with water-based cleaning solutions, or even water if necessary. The 30-round translucent polymer magazines can lock together without a magazine clamp, are 30 percent lighter than metal magazines and are corrosion proof. The ambidextrous cocking lever doubles as a forward assist and can be used to chamber a round silently.

SPECIFICATIONS

Manufacturer:	*Heckler & Koch*
Type:	*assault rifle*
Calibre:	*5.56mm*
Cartridge:	*5.56 x 45mm NATO*
Length:	*758–998mm (29.84–39.29in)*
Length of barrel:	*480mm (18.9in)*
Number of grooves:	*6*
Weight:	*3.43kg (7.54lb)*
Cyclic rate of fire:	*750rpm*
Practical rate of fire:	*200rpm*
Operation:	*gas*
Magazine capacity:	*30*
Fire mode:	*semi-, full-auto*
Muzzle velocity:	*920mps (3018fps)*
Maximum range:	*1000m (3280ft)*
Effective range:	*400m (1312ft)*
Entered service:	*1995*

G36C

For some tactical missions, subcompact dimensions are still not handy enough, especially in the field of law enforcement. Aware of this, the designers and engineers at Heckler & Koch did their best to further minimize the already shortened G36K in both dimensions and weight. The result was the G36C, a weapon with the dimensions and firepower of a submachine gun, but with the penetration capabilities of the 5.56mm round. All parts – except barrel, forehand and folding buttstock – are modular and therefore exchangeable against those of other members of the G36 product family. Picatinny Rails for the bottom and both sides of the foregrip are also available to mount a variety of aiming devices, such as a red dot aiming system (which puts a red dot onto the target at the point where the bullet will strike). The four-prong flash hider is similar to the one mounted on the G36K, but is shorter in dimensions. The low-built Picatinny Rails with deeply integrated sights allow a flat line-of-sight. The mounting of any form of optical sights is easily possible. The G36C is an extremely reliable weapon, ideally suited to counter-terrorist and law-enforcement operations, where assault teams want weapons that are reliable, accurate, have full-automatic fire and good balance. The use of polymer materials helps to reduce weight.

SPECIFICATIONS

Manufacturer:	Heckler & Koch
Type:	close-quarter rifle
Calibre:	5.56mm
Cartridge:	5.56 x 45mm NATO
Length:	500–720mm (19.68–28.34in)
Length of barrel:	228mm (8.97in)
Number of grooves:	6
Weight:	2.8kg (6.16lb)
Cyclic rate of fire:	750rpm
Practical rate of fire:	200rpm
Operation:	gas
Magazine capacity:	30
Fire mode:	semi-, full-auto
Muzzle velocity:	850mps (2789fps)
Maximum range:	400m (1312ft)
Effective range:	100m (328ft)
Entered service:	1995

G36K

In 1995, in competition with designs from other manufacturers, the Heckler & Koch 50 was selected by the German Army as the successor to the G3 rifle. The rifle is now officially known as the Heckler & Koch *Gewehr* 36 – HK G36.

The G36 is available in four main versions, adapted to different roles. All versions share the same receiver, only the length and profile of the barrel and the length of the forearm and buttstock vary. The barrel, forearm and buttstock are easily replaced at unit level, thus four different weapons may be built around a single receiver.

The G36K (K for *Kurz*, meaning "short") is an assault rifle with a shortened forearm and barrel. The barrel is fitted with a large, four-prong flash hider in place of the vortex-type found on the other versions. The dimensions of the G36K make it especially suited for use by vehicle crews, special forces and law-enforcement entry units. Intermediate in size between the older HK33K and HK53K rifles, it lacks a bayonet lug and cannot fire rifle grenades. It may be fed from 100-round magazine drums if necessary, but it will not accept the bipod intended for the MG36 light support weapon (the bipod does fit, but it cannot be kept in a collapsed position). The G36K also accepts the 40mm grenade launcher.

SPECIFICATIONS

Manufacturer:	*Heckler & Koch*
Type:	*assault rifle*
Calibre:	*5.56mm*
Cartridge:	*5.56 x 45mm NATO*
Length:	*615–858mm (24.21–33.77in)*
Length of barrel:	*320mm (13in)*
Number of grooves:	*6*
Weight:	*3.13kg (6.88lb)*
Cyclic rate of fire:	*750rpm*
Practical rate of fire:	*200rpm*
Operation:	*gas*
Magazine capacity:	*30 or 100*
Fire mode:	*semi-, full-auto*
Muzzle velocity:	*850mps (2789fps)*
Maximum range:	*400m (1312ft)*
Effective range:	*100m (328ft)*
Entered service:	*1995*

HK PDW

ollowing a NATO panel enquiry into close combat and medium-range firefight scenarios, Heckler & Koch designed a new multi-role Personal Defence Weapon (PDW) in a new calibre – 4.6 x 30mm. The German company believes that the PDW is a perfect three-in-one solution: the firepower of a submachine gun, the medium-range capabilities of an assault rifle, and pistol-like close-combat dimensions.

Because of its low weight, small dimensions and less than half of the recoil of a normal 9 x 19mm submachine gun, the PDW has the handling features of a .22 weapon. It is extremely easy to operate and control and – due to the low recoil impulse of the ammunition – very steady during burst fire, with a firing rate of 950 rounds per minute.

The PDW has an integrated retractable buttstock, and ambidextrous cocking and decocking thanks to a centrally positioned cocking lever. The integrated Picatinny Rail allows the mounting of various optical sights. A folding fore-grip makes handling and control of the PDW easy during firing. The only drawback with the PDW is the calibre of the rounds it fires. The typical 9mm submachine gun round has good stopping power, whereas the 4.6mm bullet lacks the punch of the heavier bullet. Nevertheless, the PDW is an innovative step forward in submachine gun design.

SPECIFICATIONS

Manufacturer:	*Heckler & Koch*
Type:	*submachine gun*
Calibre:	*4.6mm*
Cartridge:	*4.6 x 30mm*
Length:	*340–540mm (13.38–21.25in)*
Length of barrel:	*180mm (7in)*
Number of grooves:	*6*
Weight:	*1.5kg (3.3lb)*
Cyclic rate of fire:	*950rpm*
Practical rate of fire:	*200rpm*
Operation:	*gas*
Magazine capacity:	*20 or 40*
Fire mode:	*semi-, full-auto, three-round burst*
Muzzle velocity:	*375mps (1230fps)*
Maximum range:	*400m (1312ft)*
Effective range:	*200m (656ft)*
Entered service:	*1992*

HK21

The HK21E (E for "Export") is a lightweight, general purpose machine gun in 7.62mm calibre. It can be fired from a tripod, bipod or from the shoulder (though accuracy suffers if the latter option is chosen). The HK21's closed-bolt operation and free-floating barrel provide excellent accuracy akin to a sniper rifle when using the bipod or tripod. With its cyclic rate of fire of 800 rounds per minute (13 rounds per second) the 21E can suppress a target area, but its superior accuracy allows it to be used in ways and in roles never before envisioned for a machine gun. The HK21E provides the user with a simple, quick-change barrel capability, and the Heckler & Koch design takes the convenience and ease of the barrel change to new levels of simplicity. To change the barrel the bolt is locked open, the barrel release lever depressed with the thumb and the barrel rotated 35 degrees, and removed rearward from the weapon using only one hand. This procedure can be easily accomplished even after firing 1000 rounds, because the well-insulated barrel handle precludes the need for an asbestos glove. A special insulated spare barrel carrier is available that allows a scalding-hot barrel slung across the shoulder to be safely carried by a member of the gun crew on the battlefield. The HK21 is without doubt one of the finest light machine guns in service today.

SPECIFICATIONS

Manufacturer:	*Heckler & Koch*
Type:	*light machine gun*
Calibre:	*7.62mm*
Cartridge:	*7.62 x 51mm NATO*
Length:	*1140mm (44.88in)*
Length of barrel:	*560mm (22in)*
Number of grooves:	*4*
Weight:	*9.3kg (20.46lb)*
Cyclic rate of fire:	*800rpm*
Practical rate of fire:	*300rpm*
Operation:	*delayed blowback*
Magazine capacity:	*metal link belt*
Fire mode:	*full-auto*
Muzzle velocity:	*840mps (2756fps)*
Maximum range:	*2000m (6561ft)*
Effective range:	*800m (2624ft)*
Entered service:	*1983*

HK33

The Heckler & Koch 33 rifle is essentially a scaled-down version of the G3 designed to accept the 5.56mm cartridge. The HK33E is the first 5.56 x 45-calibre rifle to use the delayed roller-lock bolt first perfected in the G3. In semi-automatic only mode for the American market the rifle is known as the HK93. The HK33 uses exactly the same trigger, bolt and firing mechanism as the G3, but is shorter and lighter. It also has the same sighting system and method of operation.

The most common version of the rifle is equipped with steel 25-round magazines, though recently steel 30-round magazines have been introduced by Heckler & Koch for the law-enforcement and military markets. The magazines themselves are extremely durable, and will usually work after having been run over by a vehicle. Most common variants are the HK33A2 and A3, i.e. fixed and retractable stock versions respectively. The E version normally has black furniture (as shown above), though it can be supplied in a camouflage pattern or in sand colour depending on user requirements. The HK33E is available with a fixed butt, with a sliding butt and in a sniping configuration.

The SG/1 version is the sniper variant, and has a cheek pad, fixed butt, bipod and telescopic sight. As with all Heckler & Koch weapons, it is very reliable.

SPECIFICATIONS

Manufacturer:	*Heckler & Koch*
Type:	*assault rifle*
Calibre:	*5.56mm*
Cartridge:	*5.56 x 45mm NATO*
Length:	*675–865mm (26.57–34in)*
Length of barrel:	*322mm (12.67in)*
Number of grooves:	*6*
Weight:	*3.89kg (8.55lb)*
Cyclic rate of fire:	*650rpm*
Practical rate of fire:	*200rpm*
Operation:	*delayed blowback*
Magazine capacity:	*25*
Fire mode:	*semi-, full-auto, three-round burst*
Muzzle velocity:	*880mps (288/fps)*
Maximum range:	*1500m (4921ft)*
Effective range:	*550m (1804ft)*
Entered service:	*1985*

HK53

SPECIFICATIONS

Manufacturer:	*Heckler & Koch*
Type:	*carbine*
Calibre:	*5.56mm*
Cartridge:	*5.56 x 45mm NATO*
Length:	*758–998mm (29.84–39.29in)*
Length of barrel:	*480mm (18.9in)*
Number of grooves:	*6*
Weight:	*3.43kg (7.54lb)*
Cyclic rate of fire:	*750rpm*
Practical rate of fire:	*200rpm*
Operation:	*gas*
Magazine capacity:	*30*
Fire mode:	*semi-auto, full-auto*
Muzzle velocity:	*920mps (3018fps)*
Maximum range:	*1000m (3280ft)*
Effective range:	*400m (1312ft)*
Entered service:	*1973*

Heckler & Koch firearms are among the most technologically and tactically advanced weapons in the world. Using its robust and reliable delayed blowback, roller-locked bolt system, the company developed the G3 assault rifle. From this weapon the firm further developed a variety of weapons designed to meet any tactical need.

The HK33E and HK53 are modifications of the delayed blowback, roller-locked bolt operating system in weapons firing the proven and popular 5.56 x 45mm round. Common throughout each weapon group is the ability to use many interchangeable assembly groups and components. This allows personnel to be fully trained on one weapon group, but also have the knowledge to operate the entire weapon system.

The HK53 is only 50mm (1.96in) longer than the 9mm MP5 submachine gun, and thus offers the compact size and handiness of a submachine gun combined with the increased range and hard-hitting firepower of the 5.56mm round. The HK53 has a straight-line buttstock and roller-locked bolt system, which gives good control in burst or sustained fire modes. The special four-prong flash hider eliminates muzzle flash. Though originally called a submachine gun, it is in fact a very compact carbine.

MG36

The MG36 is identical in length to the G36 rifle, but the barrel is heavier and has a folding bipod.

Normally 100-round magazine drums are used, but the weapon may also be fed from standard G36 box magazines. The low mass of the bolt and ergonomic in-line relationship of the barrel and the buttstock result in a highly controllable weapon when fired on full-automatic. The G36's gas system does not direct fouling gases back into the weapon's interior like conventional gas-operated rifles, which ensures reliable operation even after firing more than 15,000 rounds without cleaning. In addition, the polymer components can easily be cleaned with water.

The MG36 has a number of ambidextrous features to facilitate left- and right-hand firing: a safety/selector lever allows for easy actuation without adjusting the firing grip, the cocking lever doubles as a forward assist and can be used to chamber a round silently, and there is an ambidextrous bolt catch button. The bolt catch itself holds the bolt to the rear on the last round fired, and can be disabled by the shooter without tools, allowing the bolt to close when the magazine is fired empty.

The MG36 has a flash hider on the muzzle, which is shaped for grenade launching. The prominent carrying handle incorporates a sight.

SPECIFICATIONS

Manufacturer:	Heckler & Koch
Type:	light support weapon
Calibre:	5.56mm
Cartridge:	5.56 x 45mm NATO
Length:	760–990mm (29.92–38.98in)
Length of barrel:	622mm (24.5in)
Number of grooves:	4
Weight:	6.85kg (15.07lb)
Cyclic rate of fire:	600rpm
Practical rate of fire:	200rpm
Operation:	gas
Magazine capacity:	30 or 100
Fire mode:	semi-, full-auto
Muzzle velocity:	762mps (2500fps)
Maximum range:	1500m (4921ft)
Effective range:	400m (1312ft)
Entered service:	1995

MP5A2

The MP5 submachine gun is the undisputed choice of the vast majority of law-enforcement special response teams and military special operations units throughout the Western world. This is because the weapon is very reliable due to the fact that it fires from a closed bolt. In the firing position, inclined surfaces on the locking piece within the bolt carrier lie between the two rollers on the bolt head and force them out into recesses in the barrel extension. After ignition, the rollers are cammed inward against the locking piece's inclined planes by rearward pressure on the bolt head. The bolt carrier's rearward velocity is four times that of the bolt head. After the bolt carrier has moved to the rear 4mm (0.15in), the rollers on the bolt head are completely in, pressure has dropped to the required levels of safety, and the two parts continue their backward movement together. To further improve reliability, several years ago the MP5's bolt head was improved and strengthened to inhibit cracking.

The MP5A2 variant is fitted with a fixed buttstock. All MP5 stocks, except those designed for the shortened MP5K series, are interchangeable. Although the fixed buttstock provides the most stable firing platform, the MP5's retractable stock is among the finest in the world, and all in all the MP5 is a superb weapon.

SPECIFICATIONS

Manufacturer:	Heckler & Koch
Type:	submachine gun
Calibre:	9mm
Cartridge:	9mm Parabellum
Length:	680mm (26.7in)
Length of barrel:	225mm (8.86in)
Number of grooves:	6
Weight:	2.55kg (5.61lb)
Cyclic rate of fire:	800rpm
Practical rate of fire:	200rpm
Operation:	delayed blowback
Magazine capacity:	15 or 30
Fire mode:	semi-, full-auto, three-round burst
Muzzle velocity:	400mps (1312fps)
Maximum range:	200m (656ft)
Effective range:	100m (328ft)
Entered service:	1964

MP5A3

ecause it fires from a closed, locked breech instead of utilizing the unlocked, open-bolt concept of most submachine guns, the MP5 is technically a "machine carbine" rather than a true submachine gun. That said, its compact size in comparison to assault rifles and the fact that it fires a pistol cartridge places it firmly in the submachine gun category. Firing from a closed bolt eliminates the "lurch" experienced with conventional open-bolt submachine guns when the trigger is pressed. From a user's point of view this allows easier and more accurate firing of the weapon, which endears the MP5 to hostage-rescue teams who require great accuracy when firing at terrorists in close proximity to hostages. Critics of the closed-bolt concept point to the increased residual heat build-up that results from a closed bolt, which can cause "cook-offs". However, because Heckler & Koch weapons are so well engineered this is an almost insignificant disadvantage.

The A3 version differs from the A2 version by having a single metal strut stock which can be slid forward to reduce the overall length of the weapon. There is a safety/selector lever above the trigger, with a choice of fire modes being semi-automatic, full-automatic and three-round burst. As well as iron sights, the MP5 range of submachine guns can be fitted with image intensifiers and aiming projectors.

SPECIFICATIONS

Manufacturer:	*Heckler & Koch*
Type:	*submachine gun*
Calibre:	*9mm*
Cartridge:	*9mm Parabellum*
Length:	*490–660mm (19.3–26in)*
Length of barrel:	*225mm (8.86in)*
Number of grooves:	*6*
Weight:	*2.55kg (5.61lb)*
Cyclic rate of fire:	*800rpm*
Practical rate of fire:	*200rpm*
Operation:	*delayed blowback*
Magazine capacity:	*15 or 30*
Fire mode:	*semi-, full-auto, three-round burst*
Muzzle velocity:	*400mps (1312fps)*
Maximum range:	*200m (656ft)*
Effective range:	*100m (328ft)*
Entered service:	*1964*

MP5K

The MP5K is the ultimate close-quarters weapon. At 2kg (4.4lb) and less than 330mm (13in) long, the MP5K is easily concealed and carried and is ideal for police and counter-terrorist use. All MP5Ks can be fitted with an optional folding buttstock, and it can also be fired from inside a specially designed briefcase.

Apart from a shorter barrel and smaller 15-round magazine, the K version (K meaning *Kurz* or short) is mechanically identical to the full-sized MP5. The MP5 series is excellent for counter-terrorist work but is less suited to general use in the field. There are two main reasons for this. First, the precision engineering required to produce Heckler & Koch submachine guns makes each gun relatively expensive (this is a definite move away from the "cheap and cheerful" submachine guns mass-produced during World War II). Second, while they are reliable weapons, they do require great care and attention to keep them fully functional. They are too well made to tolerate extended combat use in sand, mud or snow.

The MP5K is used by undercover operatives because it is easy to conceal in clothing and bags. In addition, it is an excellent weapon for plainclothes soldiers working in unmarked cars, who often require a high-volume-of-fire weapon on operations.

SPECIFICATIONS

Manufacturer:	*Heckler & Koch*
Type:	*shortened submachine gun*
Calibre:	*9mm*
Cartridge:	*9mm Parabellum*
Length:	*325mm (12.8in)*
Length of barrel:	*115mm (4.52in)*
Number of grooves:	*6*
Weight:	*2kg (4.4lb)*
Cyclic rate of fire:	*900rpm*
Practical rate of fire:	*200rpm*
Operation:	*delayed blowback*
Magazine capacity:	*15 or 30*
Fire mode:	*semi-, full-auto, three-round burst*
Muzzle velocity:	*375mps (1230fps)*
Maximum range:	*150m (492ft)*
Effective range:	*50m (164ft)*
Entered service:	*1976*

MP5K PDW

This weapon is based on the shortened MP5K sub-machine gun with the addition of a side-folding stock and a muzzle flash hider. It is designed for use by troops who would normally travel in cramped vehicles or aircraft, such as tanks or helicopters. When folded, it is small enough to fit under a car seat.

The Personal Defence Weapon (PDW) is a compact weapon whose chassis, detachable foregrip and folding stock are constructed primarily from injection-moulded polymer, thus saving weight without compromising durability. The trigger, front and rear sights, bolt handle, fire selector, magazine release, sling swivel, butt plate and retaining pins are all metal, with the barrel itself made of brass. The ambidextrous fire-selector lever is on either side of the trigger unit. The stock is almost as long as the rest of the gun, and when extended it makes the gun long enough to fire from the shoulder to increase overall accuracy.

As stated above, the sights are made of metal; the front is a blade sight with a protective shroud, while the rear is a turret sight with different apertures for different ranges. There are three lugs on the barrel for the attachment of a silencer or grenade launcher. The butt may be removed and replaced by a cap on the receiver. There is an optional two- or three-round burst facility.

SPECIFICATIONS

Manufacturer:	*Heckler & Koch*
Type:	*special forces submachine gun*
Calibre:	*9mm*
Cartridge:	*9mm Parabellum*
Length:	*368–800mm (14.48–31.5in)*
Length of barrel:	*140mm (5.5in)*
Number of grooves:	*6*
Weight:	*2.79kg (6.13lb)*
Cyclic rate of fire:	*900rpm*
Practical rate of fire:	*200rpm*
Operation:	*delayed blowback*
Magazine capacity:	*15 or 30*
Fire mode:	*semi-, full-auto, three-round burst*
Muzzle velocity:	*375mps (1230fps)*
Maximum range:	*150m (492ft)*
Effective range:	*50m (164ft)*
Entered service:	*1992*

MP5N

eveloped especially for one of America's most élite special operations troops, the US Navy Sea-Air-Land (SEAL) teams, the MP5 "Navy" model comes with an ambidextrous trigger group and threaded barrel as standard. There are also a number of accessories that can be attached to the MP5 to enhance performance in low-light conditions. The UITC Night Stalker/SO laser aiming module, for example, is a modular laser aiming device that can be mounted on a variety of firearms. This law-enforcement module contains two laser diodes and an infrared flashlight for use with night-vision equipment. The Night Stalker/SO offers the option of dual visible or dual infrared lasers which can be configured for long- and short-range settings. Both may be independently adjusted.

The Night Stalker/SO has recessed control buttons which control each sighting system separately, and have no exposed wires. The controls and quick release levers are on both sides, thus allowing for fully ambidextrous operation of the unit. Operation involves first selecting the desired laser by switching the appropriate button. The laser can then be activated by touching the activation pad. Laser blink rates may be programmed for identification purposes.

The MP5N has a collapsible stock for use in confined spaces and ease of carrying.

SPECIFICATIONS

Manufacturer:	*Heckler & Koch*
Type:	*special forces submachine gun*
Calibre:	*9mm*
Cartridge:	*9mm Parabellum*
Length:	*610–781mm (24–30.75in)*
Length of barrel:	*225mm (8.86in)*
Number of grooves:	*6*
Weight:	*3.5kg (7.7lb)*
Cyclic rate of fire:	*800rpm*
Practical rate of fire:	*200rpm*
Operation:	*delayed blowback*
Magazine capacity:	*15 or 30*
Fire mode:	*semi-, full-auto, three-round burst*
Muzzle velocity:	*283mps (928fps)*
Maximum range:	*150m (492ft)*
Effective range:	*50m (164ft)*
Entered service:	*unknown*

MP5SD

This weapon was developed for specialized applications requiring fully realized sound and flash suppression. The removable sound suppressor is integrated into the weapon's design and conforms to the normal length and profile of a conventional, unsuppressed submachine gun. The MP5SD uses an integral aluminium or optional wet technology stainless steel sound suppressor, and does not require use of subsonic ammunition for sound reduction.

Common throughout the MP5 range of weapons is the ability to use many interchangeable assembly groups and components. This provides the ability to train personnel within one weapon group and have them competent with the entire weapon system. The SD version is no different.

Heckler & Koch scope mounts can be attached to the SD without tools at special points. They ensure 100 percent return to zero and do not interfere with the use of the weapon's iron sights.

The SD1 variant has a receiver end cap and no buttstock; the SD2 variant has a fixed buttstock; the SD3 variant has a folding butt; the SD4 variant is as the D1 version with an added three-round burst facility; the SD5 is as the D2 version but with an added three-round burst facility; and the SD6 variant resembles the D3 version with an added three-round burst facility.

SPECIFICATIONS

Manufacturer:	*Heckler & Koch*
Type:	*silenced submachine gun*
Calibre:	*9mm*
Cartridge:	*9mm Parabellum*
Length:	*550mm (21.65in)*
Length of barrel:	*146mm (5.75in)*
Number of grooves:	*6*
Weight:	*2.8kg (6.16lb)*
Cyclic rate of fire:	*800rpm*
Practical rate of fire:	*200rpm*
Operation:	*delayed blowback*
Magazine capacity:	*15 or 30*
Fire mode:	*semi-, full-auto, three-round burst*
Muzzle velocity:	*285mps (935fps)*
Maximum range:	*200m (656ft)*
Effective range:	*100m (328ft)*
Entered service:	*1975*

MP5SF

The MP5SF (single fire) carbine is a semi-automatic only variant of the MP5 fitted with a trigger group that prevents full-automatic firing. It is an ideal squad vehicle carbine and is an excellent supplement or replacement for a police shotgun. It has less recoil, greater range and more ammunition capacity than a shotgun and is especially suitable for small-stature officers. It is used by military and law enforcement in 50 countries. This selective-fire weapon can be shouldered or hand-fired.

The unique features of the Heckler & Koch MP5 range of submachine guns include a free-floating cold hammer-forged barrel, stamped sheet steel receiver, fluted chamber, straight-line stock and a pistol grip with ambidextrous safety/selector lever. The bare metal surfaces of the MP5 are phosphated and coated with a black lacquer paint. This dry lacquer coating is applied with a magnetic charge and then baked onto the metal in an oven. The resulting finish is highly resistant to salt water corrosion and surface wear.

Another variant of the MP5 aimed at the law-enforcement market is the MP5/10, which is chambered for the 10mm Auto cartridge and has a carbon-fibre, reinforced straight-box magazine. It also has a dual magazine clamp to allow two magazines to be attached and rapidly switched into the firing position.

SPECIFICATIONS

Manufacturer:	*Heckler & Koch*
Type:	*submachine gun*
Calibre:	*9mm*
Cartridge:	*9mm Parabellum*
Length:	*680mm (26.7in)*
Length of barrel:	*225mm (8.86in)*
Number of grooves:	*6*
Weight:	*2.55kg (5.61lb)*
Cyclic rate of fire:	*800rpm*
Practical rate of fire:	*200rpm*
Operation:	*delayed blowback*
Magazine capacity:	*15 or 30*
Fire mode:	*semi-, full-auto, three-round burst*
Muzzle velocity:	*400mps (1312fps)*
Maximum range:	*200m (656ft)*
Effective range:	*100m (328ft)*
Entered service:	*1964*

MSG90

The MSG90 bears a close resemblance to the G3 assault rifle. It is a magazine-fed, semi-automatic rifle chambered for the NATO-standardized 7.62 x 51mm cartridge. Like most Heckler & Koch rifles and submachine guns, it uses the delayed blowback, roller-locked bolt operating system that delivers excellent accuracy and reliable performance. Most of the rifle's internal components, plus its stock, magazine and fire-control mechanism, are interchangeable with those of the G3.

The MSG90 also incorporates a number of features pertinent to a dedicated sniper rifle. For example, reinforcing ribs are welded onto both sides of the receiver directly over the slide rails, which enhance the receiver's structural integrity and lend support to the barrel/receiver interface. For quiet loading, the MSG90's receiver is equipped with a forward assist. The absence of fixed sights on the MSG90 further indicates the specialized role that it is designed to fulfil.

Another salient feature of the MSG90 is the push-pinned trigger housing. By first removing the stock, the shooter can quickly replace the semi-automatic trigger group and housing with a unit that facilitates full-automatic firing. Essentially, the MSG90 differs from the PSG-1 in its ability to be deployed as a support weapon.

SPECIFICATIONS

Manufacturer:	*Heckler & Koch*
Type:	*sniper rifle*
Calibre:	*7.62mm*
Cartridge:	*7.62 x 51mm NATO*
Length:	*1165mm (45.87in)*
Length of barrel:	*600mm (23.62in)*
Number of grooves:	*4*
Weight:	*6.4kg (14.08lb)*
Cyclic rate of fire:	*n/a*
Practical rate of fire:	*20rpm*
Operation:	*delayed blowback*
Magazine capacity:	*5 or 20*
Fire mode:	*semi-, full-auto*
Muzzle velocity:	*820mps (2690fps)*
Maximum range:	*1800m (5905ft)*
Effective range:	*450m (1476ft)*
Entered service:	*1987*

PSG-1

The PSG-1 is one of the most accurate semi-automatic sniper rifles in the world. The accuracy standard that all PSG-1s must meet is 50 rounds of match ammunition into an 80mm (3.149in) circle at a range of 300m (984ft). The PSG-1 is popular with special operations units and anti-terrorist squads. However, it is unsuited to military operations in the field for two reasons. First, it ejects the shells about 10m (32.8ft), which can easily give away a sniper's position. Second, it only can be fitted with the Hensoldt 6 x 42 sight. No other sight can be used, and the sight is only set up to be used up to a range of 600m (1968ft). Unfortunately that distance is the start of the optimal engagement range for military snipers.

With a heavy, free-floating barrel, adjustable butt, hand rest and its telescopic sight, the PSG-1 is an outstanding police sharpshooter weapon, though it is very expensive. The rifle has a system for silent bolt closing, and the trigger has an adjustable shoe to change its width to suit individual preferences. The barrel has a polygonal bore, which prevents the escape of the tiny quantities of gas that normally leak past the bullet in conventional firing. This means that the round's trajectory remains true after firing.

The PSG-1 is in use with the German anti-terrorist unit GSG 9, plus other police units around the world.

SPECIFICATIONS

Manufacturer:	*Heckler & Koch*
Type:	*sniper rifle*
Calibre:	*7.62mm*
Cartridge:	*7.62 x 51mm NATO*
Length:	*1208mm (47.56in)*
Length of barrel:	*650mm (25.6in)*
Number of grooves:	*4*
Weight:	*8.1kg (17.82lb)*
Cyclic rate of fire:	*n/a*
Practical rate of fire:	*15rpm*
Operation:	*delayed blowback*
Magazine capacity:	*5 or 20*
Fire mode:	*semi-auto*
Muzzle velocity:	*830mps (2723ft)*
Maximum range:	*600m (1968ft)*
Effective range:	*400m (1312ft)*
Entered service:	*1985*

UMP

The German firm Heckler & Koch have long dominated the marked for submachine guns with their MP5 models, and quite rightly. This design is, though, now over three decades old and so the company has for over a decade worked on the design of a new submachine gun which it hopes will prove to be just as popular as the MP5. The UMP 45 (Universal Machine Pistol calibre .45) is the final product of this development, and it does indeed look as though it will be as successful as the MP5 series.

The entire stock is made from polymer, giving the gun high strength but low weight. The buttstock can be folded onto the right side of the gun, and the whole weapon is very stable and solid to fire. Instead of the MP5's roller-delayed action, the gun has a simple blowback action and it fires from a closed bolt. Several trigger options are available, including two-round burst.

The most surprising item is the calibre: the UMP fires the .45 ACP (Automatic Colt Pistol) cartridge, and not the 9mm as used in other submachine guns. A variety of different accessories is available, including a sling, a vertical foregrip, silencers, sights and lamps. The UMP45 is delivered with a 25-round magazine as standard, but 10-round magazines are also available.

SPECIFICATIONS

Manufacturer:	Heckler & Koch
Type:	submachine gun
Calibre:	.45in
Cartridge:	45 ACP
Length:	442–675mm (17.7–27in)
Length of barrel:	200mm (7.87in)
Number of grooves:	unknown
Weight:	unknown
Cyclic rate of fire:	700rpm
Practical rate of fire:	200rpm
Operation:	blowback
Magazine capacity:	25 or 10
Fire mode:	semi-, full-auto, two-round burst
Muzzle velocity:	442mps (1450fps)
Maximum range:	200m (656ft)
Effective range:	100m (328ft)
Entered service:	not yet in service

L7A2

The British General Purpose Machine Gun (GPMG) is a successful development of the Belgian FN MAG machine gun. The GPMG can be used in the light role, but is more normally used in the sustained-fire role, being mounted on a tripod with the C2 optical sight unit. A two-man team operates the weapon, and a number of weapons are normally grouped in a specialist machine-gun platoon. The L7A2 differs in several minor, but significant, ways from the FN weapon. The gas regulator, for example, has 10 positions (the minimum rate of fire is obtained at adjustment notch "8"), the bipod legs are adjustable for height, the buttstock is made of plastic, the gas cylinder permits installation of a heavy barrel, the chrome bore plating is thicker, the sear has two bents to engage a special piston extension (for safety when cocking, should it slip accidentally from the operator's hand), and the cartridge guide pawl is a two-piece component.

Sturdy, reliable and very accurate, the L7A2 is undoubtedly the best GPMG ever fielded and has served the British Army well for over 40 years. Used on a tripod the GPMG is effective up to a range of 1800m (5905ft), though it is difficult to spot strike at this range because the tracer rounds in the ammunition belt usually burn out at a range of 1100m (3608ft).

SPECIFICATIONS

Manufacturer:	*Royal Small Arms*
Type:	*general purpose machine gun*
Calibre:	*7.62mm*
Cartridge:	*7.62 x 51mm NATO*
Length:	*1232mm (48.5in)*
Length of barrel:	*679mm (26.75in)*
Number of grooves:	*4*
Weight:	*10.9kg (23.98lb)*
Cyclic rate of fire:	*800rpm*
Practical rate of fire:	*300rpm*
Operation:	*gas*
Magazine capacity:	*metal link belt*
Fire mode:	*full-auto*
Muzzle velocity:	*838mps (2750fps)*
Maximum range:	*3500m (1148ft)*
Effective range:	*1800m (5905ft)*
Entered service:	*1963*

L86

The L86A1 Light Support Weapon (LSW) is essentially a version of the SA80 assault rifle with a longer barrel and bipod fitted on an outrigger, as well as a rear grip. The trigger has been redesigned twice, and the push button, cross-bolt safety catch has been made stiffer to operate compared to early SA80s, to prevent it being accidentally knocked into the "on" position.

As the LSW uses rotary locking, virtually no dirt ingresses the action of the gun. In addition, the bore is chrome-lined, thus cleaning in the field is fairly straightforward. That said, dirt can accumulate in the weapon through the holes in the receiver, which can present problems on the battlefield.

The recoil is very much less than with heavier-calibre weapons, which helps in recruit training and minimizes weapon movement when firing. The LSW is gas-operated, self-loading and magazine-fed with the facility for single-shot or full-automatic fire. In addition, the strength of construction enables muzzle launching of 21mm grenades. A great advantage for infantrymen is that the magazines for the SA80 and LSW are interchangeable. In addition, around 80 percent of LSW parts are interchangeable with the SA80. Each British eight-man infantry section is usually equipped with two LSWs for support.

SPECIFICATIONS

Manufacturer:	*Royal Ordnance*
Type:	*light support weapon*
Calibre:	*5.56mm*
Cartridge:	*5.56 x 45mm NATO*
Length:	*900m (35.43in)*
Length of barrel:	*646mm (25.43in)*
Number of grooves:	*6*
Weight:	*6.1kg (13.42lb)*
Cyclic rate of fire:	*700rpm*
Practical rate of fire:	*200rpm*
Operation:	*gas*
Magazine capacity:	*30*
Fire mode:	*semi-, full-auto*
Muzzle velocity:	*970mps (3182fps)*
Maximum range:	*1500m (4921ft)*
Effective range:	*400m (1312ft)*
Entered service:	*1986*

L96A1

The L96A1 has a plastic stock, a light bipod and a monopod in the butt, which allows the rifle to be laid on the target for long periods without the firer having to support the weight of the weapon. The Al bipod is of the highest quality and mounts via a quick detachable fitting, integral with the fore-end. This system has five degrees of left and right cant built into the mount, resulting in enough movement so that the rifle can be supported in a level firing position on uneven surfaces. The bipod itself has a tension-adjustable ball joint, which allows tracking of moving targets without movement of the bipod feet. The legs of the bipod are spring loaded and positively lock into each height-adjustment notch. The skid-type feet of the bipod work well on any number of surfaces.

Originally designed for the British military in the early 1980s and designated the L96A1, the rifle was upgraded in the late 1980s to enhance its reliability in arctic weather conditions. This newly modified rifle received the designation Arctic Warfare (AW) model, though it also performs well in hot, humid climates. The AW is built to military requirements, and can fire 25,000 rounds before failure. The bolt body is partially covered with shallow fluting to allow space for debris to accumulate without binding or jamming the bolt.

SPECIFICATIONS

Manufacturer:	*Accuracy International*
Type:	*sniper rifle*
Calibre:	*7.62mm*
Cartridge:	*7.62 x 51mm NATO*
Length:	*1194mm (47in)*
Length of barrel:	*655mm (25.6in)*
Number of grooves:	*4*
Weight:	*6.5kg (14.3lb)*
Cyclic rate of fire:	*n/a*
Practical rate of fire:	*10rpm*
Operation:	*bolt*
Magazine capacity:	*10*
Fire mode:	*single shot*
Muzzle velocity:	*850mps (2788fps)*
Maximum range:	*3000m (9842ft)*
Effective range:	*1000m (3280ft)*
Entered service:	*1985*

SA80

The SA80 is the standard assault rifle of the British Army. Despite its bullpup design, standard adjustable optical telescope and a pressed steel receiver, it has been plagued by problems from the beginning, and these problems persist. For example, in terms of overall reliability the SA80 does not perform well in field conditions, and in the 1991 Gulf War (the first operational deployment outside Northern Ireland) there were reports of sand clogging the trigger-mechanism housing and the gas regulator. When used in the jungles of Belize, the standard-issue British Army insect repellent melted the rifle's plastic furniture! Despite the problems, over 330,000 are in British service.

The weapon is of reasonably lightweight construction, having a pressed-steel receiver in which the bolt rides upon guide rods. This has certainly reduced manufacturing time, but has had the unfortunate result of creating a somewhat fragile weapon. The SA80's sight is the Sight Unit Small Arms Trilux (SUSAT), a short telescope with an illuminated recticle which works well enough.

A version of the SA80 is the L86A1 cadet rifle, which has a manual bolt handle in place of the gas system and a carrying handle and flip aperture sight. It is restricted to Army Cadet Force training and can be fitted with a .22RF adaptor for indoor range shooting.

SPECIFICATIONS

Manufacturer:	*Royal Ordnance*
Type:	*assault rifle*
Calibre:	*5.56mm*
Cartridge:	*5.56 x 45mm NATO*
Length:	*785mm (30.9in)*
Length of barrel:	*518mm (20.4in)*
Number of grooves:	*6*
Weight:	*3.81kg (8.38lb)*
Cyclic rate of fire:	*650–800rpm*
Practical rate of fire:	*150rpm*
Operation:	*gas*
Magazine capacity:	*30*
Fire mode:	*semi-, full-auto*
Muzzle velocity:	*940mps (3084fps)*
Maximum range:	*1000m (3280ft)*
Effective range:	*400m (1312ft)*
Entered service:	*1986*

SUPER MAGNUM

The Accuracy International Super Magnum rifle is essentially an upgraded version of its L96A1 rifle, fitted and strengthened to fire high-powered magnum cartridges. The calibres it is available in are: 7mm Remington Magnum, .300 Winchester Magnum, and the .338 Lapua Magnum. Using the Lapua cartridge the Super Magnum is capable of approaching the range of some .5in-calibre sniper rifles.

This excellent bolt-action rifle is fed from a five-round detachable magazine, and the entire rifle is centred on a large aluminium frame, upon which the action and the barrel are mounted. At the front end of the frame, a Parker Hale bipod can be attached. The heavy, free-floating barrel is supported by an aluminium frame, and the whole assembly is held in a high-impact plastic stock. To help control any muzzle jump, the barrel and butt are in a straight line, with the butt length being adjustable by the addition or removal of extension pieces.

The rifle is set up to accept a variety of scopes through a one-piece scope mount. At the end of the barrel a large muzzle brake is attached, and the heavy barrel gives the rifle excellent accuracy. The rifle is already in the service of the Netherlands as a counter-sniper weapon, and several other armies are evaluating it.

SPECIFICATIONS

Manufacturer:	*Accuracy International*
Type:	*sniper rifle*
Calibre:	*7mm, .300in, .338in*
Cartridge:	*various*
Length:	*1255mm (50in)*
Length of barrel:	*67.77mm (27in)*
Number of grooves:	*4*
Weight:	*6.8kg (14.96lb)*
Cyclic rate of fire:	*n/a*
Practical rate of fire:	*5rpm*
Operation:	*bolt*
Magazine capacity:	*5*
Fire mode:	*single shot*
Muzzle velocity:	*850mps (2788fps)*
Maximum range:	*3000m (9842ft)*
Effective range:	*1100m (3609ft)*
Entered service:	*2000*

GALIL

ollowing the Six-Day War of 1967, there were calls among the Israeli military for a lighter and handier individual weapon than the FN FAL, which was then in Israeli service. A design team led by Israel Galil tested a variety of rifles, including the AK-47, M16 and Stoner 63. It reached the conclusion that it liked the 5.56mm cartridge of the M16, but preferred the AK-47's conventional piston to the M16's direct-impingement gas system. It therefore selected one of the most up-to-date variants of the AK-47 from which to work: the Valmet M62. The Finnish firm provided the first 1000 receivers for the new rifle, which was officially adopted in 1972 and called the Galil. Insufficient quantities of the Galil were available at the time of the 1973 Yom Kippur War, so Israel was provided with large quantities of US M16 rifles.

The Galil's long magazine requires long bipod legs. These are suspended from a large casting that incorporates the gas cylinder, front sight base and front sling attachment staple. The bipod is equipped with a wire cutter that uses the bipod legs for leverage. The Galil's plastic pistol grip is very functional and was taken from the Hungarian AKM/AMD-65 rifles. Its sharp bottom flare prevents the hand from slipping, and the grip has been mounted to the receiver at precisely the correct grip-to-frame angle.

SPECIFICATIONS

Manufacturer:	*Israel Military Industries*
Type:	*assault rifle*
Calibre:	*7.62mm*
Cartridge:	*7.62 x 51mm NATO*
Length:	*810–1050mm (31.89–41.34in)*
Length of barrel:	*535mm (21in)*
Number of grooves:	*4*
Weight:	*4.4kg (9.68lb)*
Cyclic rate of fire:	*650rpm*
Practical rate of fire:	*150rpm*
Operation:	*gas*
Magazine capacity:	*25*
Fire mode:	*semi-, full-auto*
Muzzle velocity:	*850mps (2788fps)*
Maximum range:	*1000m (3280ft)*
Effective range:	*400m (1312ft)*
Entered service:	*1972*

GALIL SNIPER

The Galil 7.62mm sniping rifle was introduced by Israel Military Industries (IMI) in 1983. It was developed by the Israel Defence Force (IDF) to provide an extremely accurate sniping rifle while at the same time being very robust. It has the basic Galil rifle mechanism in 7.62mm calibre, but with special features.

The bipod is mounted on the fore-end, close to the receiver where it can be easily adjusted by the firer, and the barrel is heavier than standard. The telescope sight mount is on the side of the receiver and can be mounted and dismounted without disturbing the zeroing (a Nimrod 6 x 40 telescope sight is provided as standard).

The butt folds for ease of convenience in storage and transport, and the cheek piece and recoil pad are both adjustable. The barrel is fitted with a combined compensator and muzzle brake, which can be removed and replaced by a silencer, for which subsonic ammunition is provided. The rifle has a two-stage trigger, and the mechanism has been altered so that only semi-automatic fire will work. The standard iron sights are retained for emergency use.

The Galil is a very robust weapon: models have been buried in sand, immersed in water, driven over by trucks and generally mistreated before firing hundreds of rounds without any problems.

SPECIFICATIONS

Manufacturer:	Israel Military Industries
Type:	sniper rifle
Calibre:	7.62mm
Cartridge:	7.62 x 51mm NATO
Length:	840–1115mm (33–43.9in)
Length of barrel:	508mm (20in)
Number of grooves:	4
Weight:	6.4kg (14.08lb)
Cyclic rate of fire:	n/a
Practical rate of fire:	10rpm
Operation:	gas
Magazine capacity:	30
Fire mode:	semi-auto
Muzzle velocity:	815mps (2674fps)
Maximum range:	2000m (6561ft)
Effective range:	800m (2624ft)
Entered service:	1983

MICRO UZI

The Uzi family of submachine guns is only in limited use in Israel. The models in service are the Mini Uzi and Micro Uzi, which are mainly being used by the rappelling and fast-roping sections of counter-terrorist units. These units need a compact gun to allow them ease of movement in tight spaces, yet require a more powerful weapon than the average handgun.

The Micro Uzi has four main users in Israel: counter-terrorist units; high-ranking officers who consider it as a status symbol and want to be armed with a distinctive "combat" weapon, but not with a clumsy big and long assault rifle; Unit 669, consisting of airborne doctors and medics; and air crew personnel, especially in helicopters, since the Micro Uzi has greater firepower than a handgun, yet is in a compact and handy frame.

There are three Micro Uzi versions in use in Israel: the standard Micro Uzi, Counter-Terrorist Micro Uzi and the new Para Uzi, all of which are closed-bolt weapons.

These Counter-Terrorist and Para modified weapons have several important improvements compared to the standard version: illuminated night sights; an enlarged front and back sights block, which enables a faster target acquisition; threads along the barrel for mounting suppressors; and a cocking handle on the right side of the weapon.

SPECIFICATIONS

Manufacturer:	*Israel Military Industries*
Type:	*compact submachine gun*
Calibre:	*9mm*
Cartridge:	*9mm Parabellum*
Length:	*250–460mm (9.84–18.11in)*
Length of barrel:	*117mm (4.61in)*
Number of grooves:	*4*
Weight:	*1.95kg (4.29lb)*
Cyclic rate of fire:	*1250rpm*
Practical rate of fire:	*250rpm*
Operation:	*blowback*
Magazine capacity:	*20*
Fire mode:	*semi-, full-auto*
Muzzle velocity:	*330mps (1082fps)*
Maximum range:	*200m (656ft)*
Effective range:	*30m (98ft)*
Entered service:	*1982*

MINI UZI

The Mini Uzi is similar to the standard Uzi but is more compact and actually has a higher rate of fire (this has aroused criticism because the higher rate of fire makes the weapon harder to control when burst-firing). The Mini Uzi can be fired from an open bolt or a closed bolt and, like the standard Uzi, uses a blowback operation (whereby the breech is kept closed by the inertia of the breechblock and pressure of the recoil spring, so that, on firing, the chamber pressure "blows the bolt back" once it overcomes this inertia). The smaller size of the Mini Uzi allows it to be used easily in small, enclosed confines, such as the inside of an armoured personnel carrier.

The Mini-Uzi has a folding stock for easier concealability, and is considered an excellent weapon due to its small size and reliability. The magazine for the Mini Uzi and the standard Uzi are the same (though the Mini can also use special short magazines), and some of the parts between the two weapons are also interchangeable. The Mini Uzi has a simple wire folding stock, and has compensating slots cut into the top of the muzzle.

Some modified Micro Uzis (see page 54) are fitted with the Mini Uzi's stock, which is bigger and much more comfortable than the original Micro Uzi one. All in all, the Mini Uzi is an excellent submachine gun.

SPECIFICATIONS

Manufacturer:	*Israel Military Industries*
Type:	*compact submachine gun*
Calibre:	*9mm*
Cartridge:	*9mm Parabellum*
Length:	*360–600mm (14.17–23.62in)*
Length of barrel:	*197mm (7.75in)*
Number of grooves:	*4*
Weight:	*2.7kg (5.94lb)*
Cyclic rate of fire:	*950rpm*
Practical rate of fire:	*200rpm*
Operation:	*blowback*
Magazine capacity:	*20, 25 or 32*
Fire mode:	*semi-, full-auto*
Muzzle velocity:	*352mps (1155fps)*
Maximum range:	*150m (656ft)*
Effective range:	*70m (230ft)*
Entered service:	*1981*

NEGREV

The Negev light machine gun was developed in the late 1980s with the operational needs and specifications of the Israel Defence Force (IDF) in mind. It was designed to replace all current light machine guns in use with the IDF on all the relevant platforms: infantry, vehicle, airborne and maritime.

On the surface the Negev looks suspiciously like the Minimi, and the Israeli weapon is very close in concept to the Belgian gun. Internally, though, the two firearms vary in several technical aspects. All in all, both items are very much alike, being very accurate, reliable and lightweight. Based on IDF operational experience with both weapons over the years in adverse field conditions, the Negev proved itself to be more reliable in harsh desert conditions than the Minimi. The Negev's folding metal stock is also a big advantage over the Minimi.

The Negev is an air-cooled weapon with a rotating bolt. The mechanism uses a conventional gas and piston method of operating, with a two-piece rotary bolt. The Negev can fire from either a magazine (either Galil or M16 box magazines) or from a belt with an adapter fitted in place. The assault machine gun version has the same receiver, pistol grip and butt, but has no bipod and a shorter barrel. The Negev is a very sturdy weapon.

SPECIFICATIONS

Manufacturer:	*Israel Military Industries*
Type:	*light machine gun*
Calibre:	*5.56mm*
Cartridge:	*5.56 x 45mm NATO*
Length:	*780–1020mm (30.7–40.15in)*
Length of barrel:	*460mm (18.11in)*
Number of grooves:	*6*
Weight:	*7.5kg (16.5lb)*
Cyclic rate of fire:	*850–1000rpm*
Practical rate of fire:	*200rpm*
Operation:	*gas*
Magazine capacity:	*30, 35 or link belt*
Fire mode:	*semi-, full-auto*
Muzzle velocity:	*1000mps (3280fps)*
Maximum range:	*1500m (4921ft)*
Effective range:	*400m (1312ft)*
Entered service:	*1990*

UZI

The Uzi, one of the most famous submachine guns in the world, is a compact weapon that has a square outline and is made from steel pressings riveted and spot-welded together. It uses a blowback mechanism, but has a bolt that actually wraps around the end of the barrel. The bolt face and firing pin are some 95mm (3.75in) back from the front edge of the bolt, the rest of which surrounds the chamber and rear of the barrel. Slots are cut into the bolt to allow empty cases to pass through when being ejected. By employing this wrap-around method a large bolt can be made that takes up little space. The return spring sits around a guide rod above the level of the barrel, which extends forward of the chamber.

The large pistol grip extends beneath the centre of the body, with the trigger assembly in front of this. The ammunition feed is actually through the butt, and 25- or 32-round magazines are inserted from below the grip, a system that helps the firer replace magazines quickly.

Early models of the Uzi had a fixed wooden stock, although most have since been fitted with a folding metal example (as shown above). The grip is positioned roughly at the point of balance, which makes the weapon much easier to control when firing bursts or from one hand. The Uzi has now been in service for 50 years.

SPECIFICATIONS

Manufacturer:	Israel Military Industries
Type:	submachine gun
Calibre:	9mm
Cartridge:	9mm Parabellum
Length:	470–650mm (18.5–25.6in)
Length of barrel:	260mm (10.23in)
Number of grooves:	6
Weight:	3.75kg (8.25lb)
Cyclic rate of fire:	600rpm
Practical rate of fire:	200rpm
Operation:	blowback
Magazine capacity:	25 or 32
Fire mode:	semi-, full-auto
Muzzle velocity:	400mps (1312fps)
Maximum range:	200m (656ft)
Effective range:	50m (164ft)
Entered service:	1954

AR-70/90

This weapon was the result of the Italian Army's decision to adopt a small-bore assault rifle for its troops in the 1960s. The Beretta AR-70 family of weapons was selected, including the AR-70 assault rifle, SC-70 carbine and LM-70 light machine gun. The AR-70 copied many features of the AK-47, though with certain modifications. For example, while the AK-47 has long-stroke gas drives with a gas piston permanently attached to the bolt carrier, the AR-70 has a short-stroke gas drive with a separated gas piston. The charging handle is fixed to the bolt carrier, while the gas regulator has two positions for normal or heavy duty modes of operation.

In the late 1980s, the Italian Army decided to adopt the 5.56mm round throughout its units in line with other Western armies, and in the subsequent assault rifle trials the Beretta AR-70/90 rifle was selected. The new weapon had a number of improvements, including a strengthened receiver, a reshaped butt to give a straight-line layout, and a detachable carrying handle. There are a number of variants of this weapon, including the SC-70/90 (a folding butt version of the AR-70/90) and the SCS-70/90 (a short-barrelled variant of the SC-70/90, which has a folding butt but no gas regulator and therefore has no ability to fire rifle grenades).

SPECIFICATIONS

Manufacturer:	*Beretta*
Type:	*assault rifle*
Calibre:	*5.56mm*
Cartridge:	*5.56 x 45mm NATO*
Length:	*998mm (39.29in)*
Length of barrel:	*450mm (17.71in)*
Number of grooves:	*6*
Weight:	*3.99kg (8.77lb)*
Cyclic rate of fire:	*625rpm*
Practical rate of fire:	*150rpm*
Operation:	*gas*
Magazine capacity:	*30*
Fire mode:	*semi-, full-auto, three-round burst*
Muzzle velocity:	*930mps (3050fps)*
Maximum range:	*1000m (3280ft)*
Effective range:	*400m (1312ft)*
Entered service:	*1990 (AR-70/90)*

MODEL 12

The Beretta Model 12 submachine gun was developed in 1959 and was adopted by the Italian Army, the *Carabinieri*, and by other military and police agencies around the world. The Model 12 is a recoil-operated, selective-fire gun that operates from an open bolt. The firing pin is fixed to the bolt, which "sleeves" around the rear part of the barrel to reduce the overall length and barrel jumping during full-automatic fire. The receiver, both handles and magazine veil are made from stamped steel. The charging handle is located on the left side. The two pistol grips are located at each end of the body, and the Model 12 has a push-through selector lever just in front of and above the rear grip, behind which is a push-button safety catch. The safety catch actually unlocks the main safety system, which is a lever built into the front of the grip. Unless the grip safety is squeezed, the bolt will not move, whether it is in the cocked or uncocked state.

The Model S version, introduced in 1983, has an automatic safety catch at the front side of the grip, as well as a three-position safety/fire selector and improved butt catch operation. This version also has improved sights and has its external surfaces coated in a protective epoxy resin finish. The Model 12 may be fitted with either a side-folding metallic stock or a fixed stock.

SPECIFICATIONS

Manufacturer:	*Beretta*
Type:	*submachine gun*
Calibre:	*9mm*
Cartridge:	*9mm Parabellum*
Length:	*417–660mm (16.43–26in)*
Length of barrel:	*200mm (7.9in)*
Number of grooves:	*6*
Weight:	*3.4kg (7.48lb)*
Cyclic rate of fire:	*550rpm*
Practical rate of fire:	*200rpm*
Operation:	*blowback*
Magazine capacity:	*20, 32 or 40*
Fire mode:	*semi-, full-auto*
Muzzle velocity:	*380mps (1250fps)*
Maximum range:	*200m (656ft)*
Effective range:	*50m (164ft)*
Entered service:	*1959*

SC-70/90

This weapon is an assault carbine version of the AR-70/90. It is a light rifle ideally suited to security/police work. Essentially a folding-butt version of the AR-70/90, it has a strengthened receiver and a detachable carrying handle. Automatic models of this sort of rifle are perfect for commando missions, where long-range precision and long barrels are not needed. Because of these attributes, it is used by the *Gruppo Intervento Speciale* (GIS) of Italy, a unit which numbers only 50 members.

The SCS-70/90 is the special-purpose version of this rifle. It features the folding stock and a shorter barrel. The SC-70/90 and SCS-70/90 are in service with the COMSUBIN (Italian Navy Commandos).

Both weapons can take M16-type magazines, and are gas operated with a rotating bolt. The SCS-70/90 has no gas regulator and cannot fire rifle grenades, and the SCP-70/90 variant is similar to the SCS-70/90 but with a gas regulator and attachable grenade launcher.

The trigger mechanism of the AR-70/90 range of rifles allows single shots, three-round bursts or full-automatic fire. In addition, all variants have strong receivers and have been designed to facilitate ease of field stripping and maintenance. The bayonet shown in the photograph comes with the weapon as standard.

SPECIFICATIONS

Manufacturer:	*Beretta*
Type:	*assault rifle*
Calibre:	*5.56mm*
Cartridge:	*5.56 x 45mm NATO*
Length:	*757–986mm (29.8–38.8in)*
Length of barrel:	*450mm (17.8in)*
Number of grooves:	*6*
Weight:	*3.99kg (8.77lb)*
Cyclic rate of fire:	*700rpm*
Practical rate of fire:	*150rpm*
Operation:	*gas*
Magazine capacity:	*30*
Fire mode:	*semi-, full-auto, three-round burst*
Muzzle velocity:	*960mps (3150fps)*
Maximum range:	*1000m (3280ft)*
Effective range:	*400m (1312ft)*
Entered service:	*1990*

SPECTRE

The Spectre submachine gun was developed by the Italian company SITES in the mid-1980s. It was designed primarily for close-quarters combat, such as counter-terrorist or police operations, where compact size, instant firepower at short ranges and safety of operations are paramount. The Spectre is a recoil-operated, automatic firearm which fires from a closed bolt. The trigger group is more similar to a handgun than to a submachine gun, i.e. double-action (a firing mechanism employing a hammer, in which the hammer can be raised and cocked by the thumb and then released by the trigger; alternatively it can be raised, cocked and released by a longer pull of the trigger) without manual safety. This means that the weapon can be carried with a loaded chamber and hammer down, and then fired immediately simply by pressing the trigger.

The receiver of the Spectre is made from stamped steel and the magazine is of an unusually thick four-column design. The bolt is so designed that it acts as an air pump to push air through the barrel shroud to provide additional cooling for the barrel and action (very useful when firing long bursts). The Spectre has a top-folding stock, pistol grip and polymer forward handle. Its compact size makes it ideal for police and special forces use, especially for undercover and plainclothes operatives.

SPECIFICATIONS

Manufacturer:	SITES
Type:	police submachine gun
Calibre:	9mm
Cartridge:	9mm Parabellum
Length:	350–580mm (13.78–22.83in)
Length of barrel:	130mm (5.12in)
Number of grooves:	4
Weight:	2.9kg (6.38lb)
Cyclic rate of fire:	850rpm
Practical rate of fire:	200rpm
Operation:	blowback
Magazine capacity:	30 or 50
Fire mode:	semi-, full-auto
Muzzle velocity:	400mps (1312fps)
Maximum range:	200m (656ft)
Effective range:	50m (164ft)
Entered service:	1985

AK-101

In its effort to earn hard currency, Kalashnikov intro-duced the Hundred series, which is essentially the same as the older designs but in NATO calibres.

The operation is the tried-and tested Kalashnikov method: reloading is based on using the energy of propellant gases, which are driven into the gas cylinder located on top of the barrel. When fired, some of the propellant combustion gases, pushing the bullet along the bore channel, escape into the gas cylinder and exert pressure on the front surface of the piston. The whole group being driven rearwards, the bolt turns to the right and disengages its two locking lugs from their recesses in the receiver. The extractor claw removes the empty case from the chamber, and the ejector disposes of it through the opening in the right side of the top cover. As the bolt carrier travels farther, the single-strand recoil spring is compressed and the hammer is cocked and engaged with the auto-safety cocking cam. The cycle thus completed, the bolt group begins its return travel driven by the recoil spring. The mechanism goes forward, another round is stripped from the magazine and chambered, the bolt turns left to lock the chamber, while the bolt carrier releases the hammer from the auto-safety sear. With the hammer cocked and the bolt locked, the rifle is ready to fire again.

SPECIFICATIONS

Manufacturer:	*Kalashnikov*
Type:	*assault rifle*
Calibre:	*5.56mm*
Cartridge:	*5.56 x 45mm NATO*
Length:	*943mm (37.12in)*
Length of barrel:	*415mm (16.34in)*
Number of grooves:	*4*
Weight:	*3.4kg (7.48lb)*
Cyclic rate of fire:	*600rpm*
Practical rate of fire:	*400rpm*
Operation:	*gas*
Magazine capacity:	*30*
Fire mode:	*semi-, full-auto*
Muzzle velocity:	*910mps (2985fps)*
Maximum range:	*1000m (3280ft)*
Effective range:	*400m (1312ft)*
Entered service:	*1988*

AK-47

One of the greatest assault rifles of all time, AK-47 stands for *Avtomat Kalashnikova, Model of 1947*. The AK-47 was designed by legendary weapons designer M.T. Kalashnikov in the mid-1940s, and was adopted by the Soviet Army in 1949. It was manufactured in huge numbers, for both internal use and export. Many countries, such as Romania, Bulgaria, East Germany, China and others also manufactured clones of the AK, and it is still built around the world in its various versions.

The AK-47's fire selector/safety switch is located on the right side of the receiver, and has three positions: "Safe" (upper position), "Auto" (middle) and "Single-shot" (lower position). The safety switch is somewhat uncomfortable to operate, though. The AK features open iron sights, with the front sight adjustable for windage and the rear sight adjustable for elevation and marked in hundreds of metres. The AK's stock and grip are made of wood.

The legendary reliability of the AK comes from its simple design and overpowered gas drive. When operating in normal conditions, for example, the bolt carrier/bolt group moves at high speed and strikes hard against the rear wall of the receiver and against the front wall of the receiver on the way back. This decreases accuracy, but gives the system the power needed to operate with a fouled and dirty receiver.

SPECIFICATIONS

Manufacturer:	*Kalashnikov*
Type:	*assault rifle*
Calibre:	*7.62mm*
Cartridge:	*7.62 x 39mm M1943*
Length:	*869mm (34.21ft)*
Length of barrel:	*414mm (16.3in)*
Number of grooves:	*4*
Weight:	*4.3kg (9.46lb)*
Cyclic rate of fire:	*775rpm*
Practical rate of fire:	*400rpm*
Operation:	*gas*
Magazine capacity:	*30*
Fire mode:	*semi-, full-auto*
Muzzle velocity:	*710mps (2329fps)*
Maximum range:	*1000m (3280ft)*
Effective range:	*400m (1312ft)*
Entered service:	*1949*

AK-74

This weapon, developed for use by motorized infantry, became operational in 1974. Unlike the AKM (which was essentially a modified AK-47), the AK-74 has a number of distinctive features. The foresight bracket, for example, has two protruding cylindrical sleeves. The front one is threaded for the attachment of the recoil compensator, while the rear one has a lug with a hole for the cleaning rod. The elongated recoil compensator comprises two chambers. The first chamber is a cylinder with a hole for the bullet passage, three top holes for escape of the powder gases and two slits on the left and right of the diaphragm. The second chamber has wide openings on the right and left, and a diaphragm at the front with holes for the bullet exit. The diaphragm edges are also bevelled to ensure the directed gases escape. The butt plate is made of rubber, with transverse grooves to improve the steadiness of the weapon against the shoulder.

The main difference between this weapon and the AKM, of course, is the reduced calibre: 5.45mm. The AK-74 comes with a bayonet, and the BG15 grenade launcher can also be attached under the barrel. As with the AK-47, this weapon has been copied in numerous countries, with clones in China and the former Yugoslavia being chambered for the NATO 5.56mm cartridge.

SPECIFICATIONS

Manufacturer:	Kalashnikov
Type:	assault rifle
Calibre:	5.45mm
Cartridge:	5.45 x 39.5mm
Length:	928mm (36.53in)
Length of barrel:	400mm (15.75in)
Number of grooves:	4
Weight:	3.86kg (8.49lb)
Cyclic rate of fire:	650rpm
Practical rate of fire:	100rpm
Operation:	gas
Magazine capacity:	30
Fire mode:	semi-, full-auto
Muzzle velocity:	900mps (2953fps)
Maximum range:	900m (2952ft)
Effective range:	400m (1312ft)
Entered service:	1974

AKS-74

The AKS-74, developed for motorized infantry, became operational in 1974. It is essentially the AK-74 with a folding stock for use and storage inside confined spaces. The pistol grip, foregrip, handguard and magazine are all made from glass-filled polyamide material, which saves weight but does not compromise the weapon's overall robustness. The rifle is also used by airborne troops, though in addition to a folding metallic butt there are a number of differences from the motorized infantry model. The foregrip, handguard and magazine, for example, are made from plastic material.

An unusual feature of this weapon is the fitting of a muzzle brake to the end of the barrel, which blows the muzzle gases against deflector plates then out to the side, thus reducing recoil. This, combined with its weight, makes the AKS-74 easier to control on automatic fire mode than other similar rifles. The rifle has a plastic-covered magazine which holds 30 rounds of 5.45mm ammunition. Instead of the stock folding underneath the body, as on the AKM, it folds to the side. The AKS-74 retains the simplicity and reliability of the earlier Kalashnikov designs. Some models have been seen with image intensifying night sights, and some have been used by *Spetsnaz* special forces mounting sound suppressors and firing special subsonic rounds.

SPECIFICATIONS

Manufacturer:	*Kalashnikov*
Type:	*assault rifle*
Calibre:	*5.45mm*
Cartridge:	*5.45 x 39.5mm*
Length:	*690–928mm (27.16–36.53in)*
Length of barrel:	*400mm (15.75in)*
Number of grooves:	*4*
Weight:	*3.86kg (8.49lb)*
Cyclic rate of fire:	*650rpm*
Practical rate of fire:	*100rpm*
Operation:	*gas*
Magazine capacity:	*30*
Fire mode:	*semi-, full-auto*
Muzzle velocity:	*900mps (2953fps)*
Maximum range:	*900m (2952ft)*
Effective range:	*400m (1312ft)*
Entered service:	*1974*

AK-74

This weapon, developed for use by motorized infantry, became operational in 1974. Unlike the AKM (which was essentially a modified AK-47), the AK-74 has a number of distinctive features. The foresight bracket, for example, has two protruding cylindrical sleeves. The front one is threaded for the attachment of the recoil compensator, while the rear one has a lug with a hole for the cleaning rod. The elongated recoil compensator comprises two chambers. The first chamber is a cylinder with a hole for the bullet passage, three top holes for escape of the powder gases and two slits on the left and right of the diaphragm. The second chamber has wide openings on the right and left, and a diaphragm at the front with holes for the bullet exit. The diaphragm edges are also bevelled to ensure the directed gases escape. The butt plate is made of rubber, with transverse grooves to improve the steadiness of the weapon against the shoulder.

The main difference between this weapon and the AKM, of course, is the reduced calibre: 5.45mm. The AK-74 comes with a bayonet, and the BG15 grenade launcher can also be attached under the barrel. As with the AK-47, this weapon has been copied in numerous countries, with clones in China and the former Yugoslavia being chambered for the NATO 5.56mm cartridge.

SPECIFICATIONS

Manufacturer:	Kalashnikov
Type:	assault rifle
Calibre:	5.45mm
Cartridge:	5.45 x 39.5mm
Length:	928mm (36.53in)
Length of barrel:	400mm (15.75in)
Number of grooves:	4
Weight:	3.86kg (8.49lb)
Cyclic rate of fire:	650rpm
Practical rate of fire:	100rpm
Operation:	gas
Magazine capacity:	30
Fire mode:	semi-, full-auto
Muzzle velocity:	900mps (2953fps)
Maximum range:	900m (2952ft)
Effective range:	400m (1312ft)
Entered service:	1974

DRAGUNOV

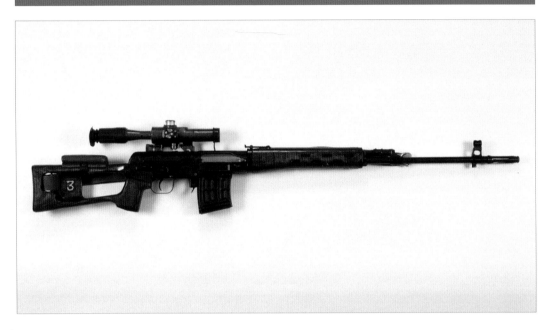

The Dragunov sniper rifle is a gas-operated, semi-automatic weapon which fires the Russian 7.62 x 54Rmm cartridge and uses a detachable 10-round magazine. Its bolt mechanism and gas recovery system are similar to those of the AK and AKM assault rifles, but because of the difference in cartridges it uses parts that are not interchangeable with the assault rifles.

The most distinguishing feature of the SVD is the open buttstock, which has a cheek pad for ease of sighting, and a telescopic sight mounted over the receiver. It also has a combination flash suppressor/compensator. In the field Russian snipers are issued with four magazines, a cleaning kit and an extra battery and lamp for the telescopic sight. The SVD fires approximately 30 rounds per minute in the semi-automatic mode, though rate of fire is dependent upon suitable targets presenting themselves, and has a maximum effective range of 1300m (4265ft) with the four-power telescope, or 800m (2624ft) without the scope. The PSO-1 optical sight has a six-degree field of view and contains an integral, infrared detection aid, and an illuminated rangefinder recticle. Ammunition types used by the Dragunov include light ball, heavy ball, steel core, tracer and anti-tank incendiary. Though now rather long in the tooth, it is still a fine sniper rifle.

SPECIFICATIONS

Manufacturer:	*State Factories*
Type:	*sniper rifle*
Calibre:	*7.62mm*
Cartridge:	*7.62 x 54Rmm*
Length:	*1225mm (48.23in)*
Length of barrel:	*622mm (24.48in)*
Number of grooves:	*4*
Weight:	*4.3kg (9.46lb)*
Cyclic rate of fire:	*n/a*
Practical rate of fire:	*20rpm*
Operation:	*gas*
Magazine capacity:	*10*
Fire mode:	*semi-auto*
Muzzle velocity:	*830mps (2723fps)*
Maximum range:	*3000m (9842ft)*
Effective range:	*1300m (4265ft)*
Entered service:	*1967*

NSV

The NSV is named after its designers – Nikitin, Sokolov and Volkov – and was adopted by the Soviet Army in mid-1970. It is a gas-operated, belt-fed, air-cooled automatic weapon with a horizontal sliding wedge breechblock and a quick-change barrel. It has a long, smooth, unfinned barrel with a conical flash suppressor, and features a rectangular stamped-and-riveted receiver.

A tripod-mounted version of the NSV is available for infantry use in a ground role, but the NSV is more commonly mounted on the turrets of main battle tanks (as shown above), such as the T-64, T-72 and T-80. When mounted on armoured fighting vehicles it is used as an anti-aircraft machine gun. When mounted on vehicles, the NSV can engage both aerial and ground targets. It fires the same 12.7 x 108mm cartridge as the older DShK model 38/46, although the NSV is 11kg (24.2lb) lighter than the earlier weapon.

The NSV has a recoil buffer inside the receiver for smooth operation and all NSVs are issued with the SPP variable magnification scope. The NSV is an extremely reliable and very powerful weapon, capable of piercing 16mm (.63in) of steel armour at a range of 500m (1640ft). It is unsophisticated, but it gets the job done and works in all weather conditions.

SPECIFICATIONS

Manufacturer:	*State Factories*
Type:	*heavy machine gun*
Calibre:	*12.7mm*
Cartridge:	*12.7 x 108mm*
Length:	*1560mm (61.42in)*
Length of barrel:	*1130mm (44.5in)*
Number of grooves:	*8*
Weight:	*25kg (55lb)*
Cyclic rate of fire:	*750rpm*
Practical rate of fire:	*250rpm*
Operation:	*gas*
Magazine capacity:	*50-round link belt*
Fire mode:	*full-auto*
Muzzle velocity:	*845mps (2772fps)*
Maximum range:	*7850m (25,754ft)*
Effective range:	*2000m (6561ft)*
Entered service:	*1970*

PKM

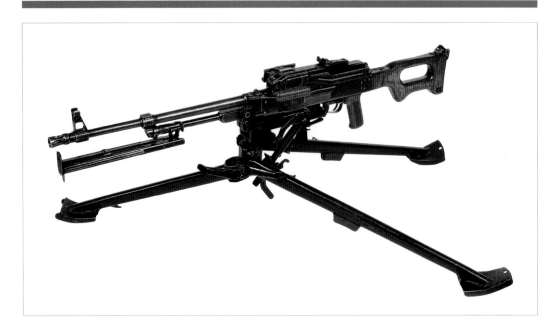

In 1961 the Kalashnikov-designed PK series of machine guns was adopted as the standard general purpose machine gun of the Red Army. Eight years later, in 1969 a product-improved version called the PKM (*Pulemyot Kalashnikova Modernizirovanniy*) was introduced, the main differences between the two models being a smooth barrel and lighter components.

The PKM has a rotating bolt with two locking lugs, similar to the AK bolt, though the PKM's bolt is larger and more robust. Because the PK fires from an open bolt, the firing pin is temporarily fixed on the bolt carrier and can be removed with the bolt. However, while the bolt is rotating along its carrier guideway, the firing pin stays locked on the bolt carrier. It will project and strike a primer while the bolt rotates to engage on the locking lugs. The PKM's bolt carrier is similar to the AK slide, though it is bigger, heavier and has a less complex shape.

The PK family has the gas piston and tube mounted beneath the barrel. The gas tube is fixed on the receiver by a spring steel latch, and it can be separated for cleaning purposes. A simple plastic pistol grip and trigger are underneath the receiver, and a folding bipod is attached to the front of the gas cylinder. As the bipod comes off with the barrel, the gun has to be supported during barrel changes.

SPECIFICATIONS

Manufacturer:	*Kalashnikov*
Type:	*general purpose machine gun*
Calibre:	*7.62mm*
Cartridge:	*7.62 x 54Rmm*
Length:	*1160mm (45.67in)*
Length of barrel:	*658mm (25.9in)*
Number of grooves:	*4*
Weight:	*9kg (19.8lb)*
Cyclic rate of fire:	*700rpm*
Practical rate of fire:	*250rpm*
Operation:	*gas*
Magazine capacity:	*metal belt*
Fire mode:	*full-auto*
Muzzle velocity:	*825mps (2706fps)*
Maximum range:	*3800m (12,467ft)*
Effective range:	*1000m (3280ft)*
Entered service:	*1969*

RPK

The RPK (*Ruchnoi Pulemet Kalashnikova* – Kalashnikov light machine gun) was developed as a light support weapon, and in Soviet service one was issued to each 10-man Red Army infantry squad (it entered service in 1959). The gun replaced the belt-fed RPD in the infantry section. Essentially the RPK is an AK-47 assault rifle with a sturdier receiver, heavier and longer, non-detachable barrel (to increase muzzle velocity), and re-contoured wooden buttstock. The sights were re-calibrated because of the longer barrel, and the rear sight has windage adjustments. The non-detachable, folding bipod (to stabilize the weapon during firing) is mounted under the muzzle. The RPK can be fed from a special 40-round box or a 75-round drum magazine, as well as from standard AK-47-type 30-round box magazines. The paratrooper version of the RPK, called the RPK-S, had a side-folding wooden buttstock.

There is no changeable barrel, which means users have to be careful to avoid overheating and excessive barrel wear. There is a cleaning rod beneath the barrel, with a gas cylinder on top of the barrel. The machine gun, like all Kalashnikov products, is very robust and works in adverse conditions. It is also light and simple to use. A little dated now, it is still in service with Russian reserve and second-line units.

SPECIFICATIONS

Manufacturer:	Kalashnikov
Type:	light machine gun
Calibre:	7.62mm
Cartridge:	7.62 x 39mm M1943
Length:	1041mm (41in)
Length of barrel:	590mm (23.22in)
Number of grooves:	4
Weight:	4.76kg (10.47lb)
Cyclic rate of fire:	600rpm
Practical rate of fire:	200rpm
Operation:	gas
Magazine capacity:	30, 40 or 75
Fire mode:	semi-, full-auto
Muzzle velocity:	734mps (2400fps)
Maximum range:	3000m (9842ft)
Effective range:	1500m (4921ft)
Entered service:	1959

RPK-74

J ust as the RPK is the squad machine-gun version of the AK-47 assault rifle, the RPK-74 is a machine-gun version of the AK-74 assault rifle, firing the same ammunition. The RPKS-74 is a folding-stock version of the weapon. Instead of the prominent muzzle brake used on the AK-74, the machine gun version has a short flash suppressor. As can be seen in the photograph above, the magazine is longer than that normally used on the AK-74, though the different-sized magazines are interchangeable. The RPK-74 has a bipod, though it is high-set to accommodate the longer magazine. It also has a drop-curved machine-gun butt which gives a grip for the non-firing hand.

The 5.45mm round of the RPK-74 has a considerably higher muzzle velocity than the 7.62mm round of the RPK family of weapons. However, both groups probably have the same maximum range – 2500m (8202ft) – and an effective range of 800m (2624ft). Unlike the RPK, the RPK-74 is compatible with the front-firing ports of the BMP infantry vehicle. Since its introduction in the mid-1970s, the RPK-74 has become the standard squad machine gun in Soviet (now Russian) motorized rifle units. It is replacing both the RPK and PKM, which are both 7.62mm weapons. Airborne squads are equipped with the RPKS-74.

SPECIFICATIONS

Manufacturer:	*Kalashnikov*
Type:	*light machine gun*
Calibre:	*5.45mm*
Cartridge:	*5.45 x 39.5mm*
Length:	*1060mm (41.73in)*
Length of barrel:	*616mm (24.25in)*
Number of grooves:	*4*
Weight:	*4.6kg (10.12lb)*
Cyclic rate of fire:	*650rpm*
Practical rate of fire:	*200rpm*
Operation:	*gas*
Magazine capacity:	*30, 40, 45*
Fire mode:	*semi-, full-auto*
Muzzle velocity:	*960mps (3150fps)*
Maximum range:	*2500m (8202ft)*
Effective range:	*800m (2624ft)*
Entered service:	*1974*

CIS 50MG

This heavy machine gun fires from an open bolt and is capable of both semi- and full-automatic fire. The left- or right-hand ammunition feed facility (it feeds a belt in at each side) allows quick changeover of ammunition in the field. In addition, the gun has a quick-change barrel with a fixed headspace, which allows the barrel to be changed within seconds without any adjustment of headspace. As well as the iron sights, the 50MG can accommodate a reflex sight that allows moving or stationary targets to be engaged effectively, and there is a night sight for firing in low-light conditions. The weapon has been designed for easy maintenance without the need for special tools.

The 50MG has a number of mounting options, including a standard M3 tripod, a pintle mount that can be easily adapted for mounting on vehicles and naval craft, and a softmount which enhances controlability and accuracy by reducing recoil.

Tactically, the air-cooled 50MG can be used for a number of roles, including fire support against infantry, vehicle protection, and helicopter armament. The weapon fires standard NATO 12.7mm ammunition, as well as Saboted Light Armour Penetrator (SLAP) rounds, which can penetrate armour plate up to 25mm (.98in) thick up to a range of 1km (.6 miles).

SPECIFICATIONS

Manufacturer:	*Singapore Technologies Kinetics*
Type:	*heavy machine gun*
Calibre:	*12.7mm*
Cartridge:	*.50 Browning*
Length:	*1670mm (66in)*
Length of barrel:	*1141mm (45in)*
Number of grooves:	*6*
Weight:	*30kg (66lb)*
Cyclic rate of fire:	*600rpm*
Practical rate of fire:	*200rpm*
Operation:	*gas*
Magazine capacity:	*disintegrating link belt*
Fire mode:	*semi-, full-auto*
Muzzle velocity:	*890mps (2920fps)*
Maximum range:	*6800m (22,309ft)*
Effective range:	*1830m (6004ft)*
Entered service:	*1988*

SAR 21

The bullpup configuration is now a firm favourite among assault rifle manufacturers, and Singapore Technologies Kinetics has followed the trend by producing the SAR 21 5.56mm model. It features an integrated 1.5 x Optical Scope and Laser Aiming Device for speedy target acquisition. The SAR 21 makes use of high-strength plastics and composites throughout, making it light and extremely rugged. For added protection for the firer, the weapon has a high-pressure vent hole at the chamber and a composite plate at the cheek rest. The whole gun has been ergonomically designed, has excellent balance and combines high accuracy with low recoil.

Maintenance in the field is made easier by the weapon's modular design. The gun breaks down into five sections – barrel group, bolt group, upper receiver group, lower receiver group and magazine – making field stripping and cleaning easy.

The SAR 21 has a number of optional extras, including a laser-aiming device, a visible infrared option, a blank-firing attachment, and bore-sighting equipment. The standard combat sight is located above the optical scope and provides back-up aiming for the soldier. The SAR 21 is a well-designed weapon, though whether it will achieve export sales in a competitive market remains to be seen.

SPECIFICATIONS

Manufacturer:	*Singapore Technologies Kinetics*
Type:	*assault rifle*
Calibre:	*5.56mm*
Cartridge:	*5.56 x 45mm*
Length:	*805mm (31.69in)*
Length of barrel:	*508mm (20in)*
Number of grooves:	*6*
Weight:	*4.28kg (9.41lb)*
Cyclic rate of fire:	*650rpm*
Practical rate of fire:	*150rpm*
Operation:	*gas*
Magazine capacity:	*40*
Fire mode:	*semi-, full-auto*
Muzzle velocity:	*940mps (3084fps)*
Maximum range:	*800m (2624ft)*
Effective range:	*460m (1509ft)*
Entered service:	*unknown*

ULTIMAX

The Ultimax is a very lightweight and mobile light machine gun. It is a gas-operated, rotating-bolt, fully automatic magazine-fed firearm that fires from an open bolt. The gas system has a three-position gas regulator. The overall action design allows the bolt carrier/bolt group to travel all the way back without being stuck into the rear of the receiver, which helps to reduce recoil and improves accuracy. The original Ultimax 100 had a fixed, heavy, air-cooled barrel, but the current Ultimax Mk 3 version has a quick-change detachable barrel available in two lengths: standard – 508mm (20in); and short – 330mm (13in). The buttstock is also detachable and this, combined with its light weight and low recoil, means the Ultimax can be fired from a standing position if necessary, thus making it suitable for close combat and urban operations (though accuracy without the buttstock is reduced). In addition, the pistol grip just forward of the drum magazine facilitates firing from a standing position.

The Ultimax can be fed from 100-round drum magazines or from M16-type box magazines that hold 20 or 30 rounds. The 100-round magazines are ideal for sustained fire, but because of their powerful springs can be reloaded only with the help of magazine-loading tools. As with the SAR 21, the company is hoping for substantial export sales.

SPECIFICATIONS

Manufacturer:	*Singapore Technologies Kinetics*
Type:	*light machine gun*
Calibre:	*5.56mm*
Cartridge:	*5.56 x 45mm NATO*
Length:	*1024mm (40.31in)*
Length of barrel:	*508mm (20in)*
Number of grooves:	*6*
Weight:	*4.9kg (10.78lb)*
Cyclic rate of fire:	*500rpm*
Practical rate of fire:	*200rpm*
Operation:	*gas*
Magazine capacity:	*20, 30 or 100*
Fire mode:	*full-auto*
Muzzle velocity:	*970mps (3182fps)*
Maximum range:	*1500m (4921ft)*
Effective range:	*400m (1312ft)*
Entered service:	*1982*

K2

The Daewoo K1 and K2 are the infantry weapons of the South Korean Army, which replaced the US M16A1 assault rifle in South Korean service. The K2 is a select-fire, gas-driven, rotating-bolt firearm which has a bolt/bolt carrier assembly very similar to the one found on the M16. The main difference, though, is that in place of the gas expansion chamber the K2 bolt carrier has a cut slot. In this slot is inserted the rear part of the gas rod, with the gas piston attached to the forward part of the gas rod. In addition, the K2 does not have the recoil buffer that is found on the M16. The receiver is of folding design, and the charging handle is installed on the right side of the bolt carrier. The polymer buttsock folds to the right side of the weapon. The gas system can be tailored for a number of options by means of a four-position switch: rifle grenade firing (the gas port is closed completely); for operations in normal conditions; for operations in adverse conditions; and in conditions of extreme heat.

The K1A1 is a compact version of the K2, which resembles a shortened K2 but uses direct gas impingement on the bolt carrier instead of a gas piston. It has a telescopic stock and shorter barrel. Like the K2 it is also a selective-fire weapon with a three-round burst facility. The specifications at right are for the K2.

SPECIFICATIONS

Manufacturer:	*Daewoo*
Type:	*assault rifle*
Calibre:	*5.56mm*
Cartridge:	*5.56 x 45mm NATO*
Length:	*730–980mm (28.74–38.58in)*
Length of barrel:	*465mm (18.3in)*
Number of grooves:	*6*
Weight:	*3.26kg (7.17lb)*
Cyclic rate of fire:	*800rpm*
Practical rate of fire:	*150rpm*
Operation:	*gas*
Magazine capacity:	*30*
Fire mode:	*semi-, full-auto, three-round burst*
Muzzle velocity:	*920mps (3018fps)*
Maximum range:	*2600m (8530ft)*
Effective range:	*550m (1804ft)*
Entered service:	*1987*

AMELI

The Ameli machine gun was developed by the CETME (now called Empresa Nacional Santa Barbara) company of Spain in 1982, and is in use with the Spanish Army as a standard squad fire-support weapon. Externally similar to the German MG3 machine gun, internally it is much closer to the CETME Model L assault rifle (or Heckler & Koch HK21 machine gun), having a similar, roller, delayed-blowback action.

The Ameli is fired from an open bolt. The barrel is of the quick-change type and it is fed from disposable plastic boxes that can contain either 100 or 200 rounds in belt form. The cyclic rate of fire can be adjusted by means of interchangeable bolts, much like the MG3. With the lighter bolt the rate of fire is about 1200 rounds per minute; with the heavier bolt the rate of fire is about 850–900 rounds per minute. The gun has conventional aperture and post sights, though a night sight can be fitted to the receiver. The Ameli can be vehicle or tripod mounted depending on tactical needs. The weapon is a compact squad automatic weapon which fires NATO 5.56mm ammunition, and has a carrying handle positioned above the rear of the barrel. It has a plastic stock, pistol grip and a flash hider. Despite being a weapon of the 1980s, its lineage can be traced back to the German MG42 of World War II.

SPECIFICATIONS

Manufacturer:	*Santa Barbara*
Type:	*squad automatic weapon*
Calibre:	*5.56mm*
Cartridge:	*5.56 x 45mm NATO*
Length:	*970mm (38.19in)*
Length of barrel:	*400mm (15.75in)*
Number of grooves:	6
Weight:	*5.2kg (11.44lb)*
Cyclic rate of fire:	*1200rpm*
Practical rate of fire:	*400rpm*
Operation:	*delayed blowback*
Magazine capacity:	*100- or 200-round belt*
Fire mode:	*full-automatic*
Muzzle velocity:	*875mps (2870fps)*
Maximum range:	*2000m (6561ft)*
Effective range:	*800m (2624ft)*
Entered service:	*1982*

CETME

The CETME assault rifle has its origins in the years following World War II, when many German arms designers were, not surprisingly, out of work. Some found employment with Spain's *Centro de Estudios Tecnicos de Materiales Especiales* – CETME (Special Materials Technical Studies Centre). Drawing on their vast wartime experience with the German StG-41 and StG-45 automatic rifles, they designed two prototypes that utilized a blowback/locking roller mechanism. The new weapon was called the Model A and was a reliable and popular weapon.

The latest version of the CETME is a semi-automatic, delayed-blowback gun that utilizes a locking roller to delay the blowback action of the bolt carrier until the pressure in the barrel is reduced to a point where the blowback force is not mechanically harmful. This is a relatively unique feature in military rifles, since most semi-automatics are operated by a separate gas cylinder. The bolt carrier rides a rail on either side of the stainless steel cast receiver, and the forward tube of the bolt carrier sub-assembly rides in its own tube located above the barrel, which also houses the charging handle and a cleaning kit. Like most modern assault rifles, the CETME uses synthetic material for its furniture. There are a number of variants, including the Model LC carbine version and Model LI export model.

SPECIFICATIONS

Manufacturer:	CETME
Type:	assault rifle
Calibre:	5.56mm
Cartridge:	5.56 x 45mm NATO
Length:	925mm (36.42in)
Length of barrel:	400mm (15.75in)
Number of grooves:	6
Weight:	3.4kg (7.48lb)
Cyclic rate of fire:	700rpm
Practical rate of fire:	200rpm
Operation:	delayed blowback
Magazine capacity:	12 or 30
Fire mode:	semi-, full-auto
Muzzle velocity:	875mps (2870fps)
Maximum range:	1500m (4921ft)
Effective range:	550m (1804ft)
Entered service:	1984

Z-84

The Z-84 submachine gun was developed in the mid-1980s by the Spanish company Star as a compact, lightweight and powerful weapon. Unlike its predecessors, the Z-62 and Z-70/B, the Z-84 is available only in 9mm Luger/Parabellum calibre.

The Z-84 has a stamped steel, two-piece receiver with the magazine housing built into the pistol grip. The bolt is of the wrap-around type, which when in the forward position sleeves around the barrel. The bolt rides on two guide rails and has significant clearance between its sides and the receiver walls, which allows the mechanism to work despite serious fouling. The Z-84 fires from an open bolt (when the bolt is held back from the empty chamber in the cocked condition), and its feed system is designed to accommodate the firing of ammunition used in police operations to achieve better stopping power, such as Soft-Point and Hollow-Point rounds.

The fire-mode selector is located at the left wall of the receiver, and allows for single shots or full-automatic fire depending on the requirement. The two-position flip-up aperture rear sights are graduated for ranges between 100m (328ft) and 200m (656ft). The folding metallic buttstock flips up and forward when not in use. The ejection port is on top of the receiver.

SPECIFICATIONS

Manufacturer:	Star
Type:	submachine gun
Calibre:	9mm
Cartridge:	9mm Parabellum
Length:	410–615mm (16.14–24.21in)
Length of barrel:	215mm (8.46in)
Number of grooves:	6
Weight:	3kg (6.6lb)
Cyclic rate of fire:	650rpm
Practical rate of fire:	200rpm
Operation:	blowback
Magazine capacity:	25 or 30
Fire mode:	semi-, full-auto
Muzzle velocity:	400mps (1312fps)
Maximum range:	150m (492ft)
Effective range:	50m (164ft)
Entered service:	1984

SG550

The SIG SG550 is the official rifle of the Swiss Army, being called the *Sturmgewehr* 90, and replaced the *Sturmgewehr* 57. The SG550 is an improved version of the SG540, which was developed in competition to meet Swish Army requirements in 1984. There is a civilian version of the rifle which is not automatic, and another variant is the SG551, which is slightly shorter than the 550 and is aimed at the police user.

The SG550 was tested under extreme conditions, including winter trials in the Alps. It is designed to reduce the amount of mud, dirt and sand that can get into the working parts, and its gas valve has two settings to ensure reliable cycling under the most extreme conditions (if need be, the user can close the bolt manually).

The SG550 has three modes of fire, including single-shot, three-round burst and full-automatic. In addition, it has special studs and slots in the magazine so that two or three magazines can be clipped together side-by-side. This allows the changing of the magazine by simply pulling the assembly out, shifting it sideways and pushing in the new magazine. The rifle has a folding stock and all features are ambidextrous. The rifle has a night sight on both the front and rear sights, and can mount a scope and light intensifier or infrared sights as well.

SPECIFICATIONS

Manufacturer:	SIG
Type:	assault rifle
Calibre:	5.56mm
Cartridge:	5.56 x 45mm NATO
Length:	772–998mm (30.39–39.29in)
Length of barrel:	528mm (20.79in)
Number of grooves:	6
Weight:	4.1kg (9lb)
Cyclic rate of fire:	700rpm
Practical rate of fire:	150rpm
Operation:	gas
Magazine capacity:	20 or 30
Fire mode:	semi-, full-auto, three-round burst
Muzzle velocity:	980mps (3215fps)
Maximum range:	1000m (3280ft)
Effective range:	400m (1312ft)
Entered service:	1986

SSG 3000

The Swiss company SIG produce excellent weapons, and this sniper rifle is no exception. The SSG 3000 is based on the equally superb 200STR target rifle, and fulfils a number of requirements: performance, out-of-the-box accuracy, and perfect integration with the shooter. The latter is guaranted by an ultra-rugged McMillan fibreglass stock that is fully adjustable. The two-stage trigger is also fully adjustable for reach, travel, take-up and weight to fit any shooter's preference.

The SSG 3000 also features a barrel interchange capability (a replacement barrel can be installed in less than two minutes). Other standard features on the SSG 3000 include six massive locking lugs on the bolt, an oversized bolt knob, a tapered, hammer-forged barrel with a flash suppressor, a drop-free five-round magazine, a scope mounting rail machined directly into the steel receiver, and a rail-mounting system on the forearm for bipods or hand stops. The bolt locks directly into the barrel, which has no iron sights but has a muzzle compensator. The barrel and receiver are joined by screw clamps, while the trigger unit and magazine consist of one forged assembly which slots into the receiver. The fore-end is ventilated, and the trigger unit and magazine comprise one forged assembly. All in all this is a first-class sniper rifle.

SPECIFICATIONS

Manufacturer:	SIG
Type:	sniper rifle
Calibre:	7.62mm
Cartridge:	7.62 x 51mm NATO
Length:	1180mm (46.45in)
Length of barrel:	610mm (24in)
Number of grooves:	6
Weight:	5.4kg (11.88lb)
Cyclic rate of fire:	n/a
Practical rate of fire:	5rpm
Operation:	gas
Magazine capacity:	bolt
Fire mode:	single shot
Muzzle velocity:	820mps (2690fps)
Maximum range:	3000m (9842ft)
Effective range:	1000m (3280ft)
Entered service:	1992

SSG550 SNIPER

The SIG SG550 Sniper is a semi-automatic variant of the famous SIG SG550/Stg 90 assault rifle, which seems to be aimed primarily at the civilian market. For example, it is one of the few 5.56mm-calibre sniper rifles around, and for this reason seems suited to police and counter-terrorist units. In essence it is a good short- to medium-range rifle more suited to police or anti-terrorist work than to use in the field. Because it is semi-automatic, a shooter is capable of quick and accurate follow-up shots.

Developed from the SG550 assault rifle, accuracy is improved by the addition of a sensitive double-pull trigger, and also a heavy, extended barrel. A bipod is standard, as is a fully adjustable butt with a cheek rest and a hand stop on the pistol grip. There are no iron sights fitted to this rifle and no muzzle attachments.

The SG550/551SP rifles are commercial versions of the SG550 and 551 respectively, and are intended as sporting weapons or for police and security use. They are restricted to semi-automatic firing and cannot be converted to fire full-automatic. The SIG552 Commando is an ultra-short semi-automatic version of the SG551 SWAT (Special Weapons And Tactics), with a cheek rest and other controls arranged for ambidextrous use. As with all SIG weapons, these rifles are extremely accurate.

SPECIFICATIONS

Manufacturer:	SIG
Type:	sniper rifle
Calibre:	5.56mm
Cartridge:	5.56 x 45mm NATO
Length:	905–1130mm (35.7–44.5)
Length of barrel:	650mm (25.6in)
Number of grooves:	6
Weight:	7.02kg (15.44lb)
Cyclic rate of fire:	n/a
Practical rate of fire:	15rpm
Operation:	gas
Magazine capacity:	20 or 30
Fire mode:	semi-auto
Muzzle velocity:	980mps (3215fps)
Maximum range:	1500m (4921ft)
Effective range:	800m (2624ft)
Entered service:	1985

CAR15

M16 rifles variants, including both the M16A1 and
the CAR15, first arrived in Israel during the Yom
Kippur War in 1973. Soon after the war the
Israel Defence Force (IDF) adopted the Galil assault rifle as
its standard-issue weapon, so the M16 did not see much
service with the IDF during the 1970s. However, several
élite units did test the M16A1, and deployed it in urban
counter-terror applications.

Following the success of the M16A1, its smaller brother –
the CAR15 – entered service in the late 1970s and was an
immediate success. Surprisingly, the first CAR15
configuration to enter IDF service was not the standard
version but the CAR15/M203 grenade launcher
combination, which was much more comfortable than the
few AK47/M203 and Galil/M203 combinations.

The CAR15 model used by the IDF is unique. The first
CAR15 models used by the US in the early 1960s – the
XM177E1 and XM177E2 – had a 254mm (10in) barrel,
which was too short and resulted in sporadic operation. Due
to the short barrel, the early CAR15 models also had an
excessive muzzle flash, which was a major tactical
disadvantage during night-time operations. In order to solve
these two issues, the weapons were fitted with a flash
suppressor at the tip of the barrel.

SPECIFICATIONS

Manufacturer:	Colt
Type:	carbine
Calibre:	5.56mm
Cartridge:	5.56 x 45mm NATO
Length:	757–838mm (29.8–33in)
Length of barrel:	370mm (14.5in)
Number of grooves:	6
Weight:	2.64kg (5.8lb)
Cyclic rate of fire:	700rpm
Practical rate of fire:	250rpm
Operation:	gas
Magazine capacity:	20 or 30
Fire mode:	semi-, full-auto, three-round burst
Muzzle velocity:	921mps (3022fps)
Maximum range:	1000m (3280ft)
Effective range:	350m (1148ft)
Entered service:	1978

COLT COMMANDO

The Colt Commando was developed as a result of the US experience during the Vietnam War, when it was discovered there was a need for a short carbine similar in size to a submachine gun but which fired rifle ammunition. The Commando is similar to the M16 assault rifle, having the same light alloy construction, rotating bolt action, and utilizing a non-reciprocating charging handle at the rear of the receiver. Because of this, most component parts are interchangeable with the M16. Due to the recoil spring being located inside the butt, the Commando cannot be equipped with a side- or underfolding stock without some redesigning. Current Colt Commando assault carbines are issued with standard M16-type 30-round magazines, but any other M16-compatible magazine can be used, including the 100-round Beta-C dual drums.

The M6 version uses a shorter barrel, plus a shorter stock, making it close in size to most submachine guns, and is ideal for close-quarter combat, yet also has a greater range. The M6 provides the individual soldier operating in close quarters with the capability to engage targets at extended range with accurate, lethal fire.

The Commando has entered service with US special forces, and is also favoured by Israeli élite units. The Israeli version is described on page 82.

SPECIFICATIONS

Manufacturer:	Colt
Type:	carbine
Calibre:	5.56mm
Cartridge:	5.56 x 45mm NATO
Length:	762mm (30in)
Length of barrel:	292mm (11.5in)
Number of grooves:	6
Weight:	2.43kg (5.38lb)
Cyclic rate of fire:	700rpm
Practical rate of fire:	200rpm
Operation:	gas
Magazine capacity:	30
Fire mode:	semi-, full-auto
Muzzle velocity:	921mps (3022fps)
Maximum range:	1000m (3280ft)
Effective range:	350m (1148ft)
Entered service:	1969

M14

The design of the M14 was first conceived during the final years of World War II. US airborne units wanted a weapon with the lightness and select-fire capabilities of the M1 Carbine, but with the killing power of the M1 Rifle. In May 1944, the development of the new rifle began. The requirements were: it had to weigh no more than 4.1kg (9lb), it had to be capable of selective semi- or full-automatic fire, it had to mount a bipod, it should have at least a 20-round magazine, it must have a folding stock to minimize length, it had to have the capability to launch rifle grenades, and it must use the same basic action as the M1.

The M14 entered service in May 1957 and proved to be a very accurate, reliable, durable and hard-hitting weapon. However, it did not fulfil all the design requirements. Because the 7.62mm NATO round is so powerful, most M14 selector levers were replaced with a special selector to allow only semi-automatic fire, thus doing away with the full-automatic capability. Some criticized the M14 for being too heavy and cumbersome, but many troops liked it for the man-stopping capability of the 7.62mm round. In all 1.5 million were built by the time production ended.

The M14 was subsequently rebuilt into a National Match rifle, in which role it still performs today with outstanding accuracy and reliability.

SPECIFICATIONS

Manufacturer:	*Springfield*
Type:	*assault rifle*
Calibre:	*7.62mm*
Cartridge:	*7.62 x 51mm NATO*
Length:	*1121mm (44.14in)*
Length of barrel:	*559mm (22in)*
Number of grooves:	*4*
Weight:	*3.88kg (8.53lb)*
Cyclic rate of fire:	*750rpm*
Practical rate of fire:	*150rpm*
Operation:	*gas*
Magazine capacity:	*20*
Fire mode:	*semi-, full-auto*
Muzzle velocity:	*853mps (2800fps)*
Maximum range:	*1500m (4921ft)*
Effective range:	*550m (1804ft)*
Entered service:	*1957*

M16A2

eneral dissatisfaction with the M14 and subsequent
numerous studies prompted the US Army to call
for the development of a lightweight weapon
capable of firing a burst of small-calibre bullets with a
controlled dispersion pattern. As a result, the Armalite
AR-15 was adopted by the Secretary of Defense as the
5.56mm M16 rifle. There were a number of problems
encountered during initial fielding, not least due to the
weapon being sold as a self-cleaning gun. However, better
training, preventive maintenance and several design changes
resulted in the weapon that has become the standard-issue
rifle of the US Army, with some 3,690,000 having been
manufactured to date. The M16 is a good rifle, but requires
careful and regular maintenance to keep it in working order.

The M16A2 version, which was re-rifled to suit the
NATO-standard 5.56mm bullet, fires a three-round burst in
addition to semi-automatic operation and full-automatic
mode. The system incorporates an adjustable rear sight
which corrects for both wind and elevation, a heavier barrel
with 1-in-7 rifling, and a muzzle compensator to prevent
muzzle climb during semi-automatic operation. The M16A2
can also fire 40mm grenades when equipped with the M203
grenade launcher, which is attached to the underside of the
barrel. The M203 replaced the M79 grenade launcher.

SPECIFICATIONS

Manufacturer:	Colt and Fabrique Nationale
Type:	assault rifle
Calibre:	5.56mm
Cartridge:	5.56 x 45mm NATO
Length:	1000m (39.37in)
Length of barrel:	508mm (20in)
Number of grooves:	6
Weight:	3.4kg (7.48lb)
Cyclic rate of fire:	800rpm
Practical rate of fire:	150rpm
Operation:	gas
Magazine capacity:	30
Fire mode:	semi-, full-auto, three-round burst
Muzzle velocity:	948mps (3110fps)
Maximum range:	1500m (4921ft)
Effective range:	550m (1804ft)
Entered service:	1982

M2

The Browning M2 .5in (12.7mm) is a World War II-era automatic, belt-fed, air-cooled weapon. It has a back plate with spade grips, a leaf-type rear sight, flash suppressor and a spare barrel assembly. By repositioning some of the component parts, ammunition may be fed from either the left or right side. The M2 is capable of single-shot as well as automatic fire.

Today, the M2 can be found mounted on vehicles as an anti-personnel and anti-aircraft weapon. Associated components are the M63 anti-aircraft mount and the M3 tripod mount, both of which provide stable platforms. The M2 .5in flexible version is used as a ground weapon on the M3 tripod mount, or on various US Navy mounts.

Tactically, the M2 provides suppressive fire for offensive and defensive purposes, and can be used effectively against personnel, light armoured vehicles, low, slow-flying aircraft, and small boats. Its 12.7mm round also has good penetrative power against brickwork and masonry. Amazingly, because of its slow rate of fire and its traversing and elevating mechanism, the M2 was also used to a very limited extent as a sniper weapon during the Vietnam War against fixed installations, such as firebases. The M2 is among the greatest machine guns of all time, and will continue to serve well into the twenty-first century.

SPECIFICATIONS

Manufacturer:	*Browning*
Type:	*heavy machine gun*
Calibre:	*12.7mm*
Cartridge:	*.50 Browning*
Length:	*2559mm (65in)*
Length of barrel:	*1143mm (45in)*
Number of grooves:	*8*
Weight:	*38.1kg (83.82lb)*
Cyclic rate of fire:	*450–575rpm*
Practical rate of fire:	*300rpm*
Operation:	*recoil*
Magazine capacity:	*110-round metal link belt*
Fire mode:	*single shot, full-auto*
Muzzle velocity:	*893mps (2930fps)*
Maximum range:	*6800m (22,309ft)*
Effective range:	*1830m (6004ft)*
Entered service:	*1933*

M24

Designed for and used by the United States military, the M24 is also very popular with US Special Weapons And Tactics (SWAT) teams across the USA, and with international military and government agencies. Based on Remington's legendary Model 700(tm) and 40X(tm) rifles, famous for their "out of the box" accuracy, the M24 has quickly gained a reputation for precision among the sniper system community.

The M24 is a conventional-looking bolt-action rifle with a six-shot integral magazine. The stock has an adjustable butt plate and is made from synthetic composite materials with metal-mounting components. The bipod is also fully adjustable to increase accuracy.

An essential element in the M-24's accuracy is its heavy, hammer-forged, stainless-steel barrel. The barrel's unique 5-R rifling delivers the combined advantages of reduced bullet deformation and metallic fouling, even-pressure curves, higher bullet velocities and longer barrel accuracy life. Additionally, the M-24's aramid fibre-reinforced, fibreglass stock with an aluminium bedding block provides exceptional strength and dimensional stability in all weather conditions. Combined with its sophisticated sighting options, the M-24 Sniper Weapon System remains the standard against which all sniper systems are compared.

SPECIFICATIONS

Manufacturer:	*Remington*
Type:	*sniper rifle*
Calibre:	*7.62mm*
Cartridge:	*7.62 x 51mm NATO*
Length:	*1092mm (43in)*
Length of barrel:	*610mm (24in)*
Number of grooves:	*4*
Weight:	*5.49kg (12.1lb)*
Cyclic rate of fire:	*n/a*
Practical rate of fire:	*10rpm*
Operation:	*bolt*
Magazine capacity:	*6*
Fire mode:	*single shot*
Muzzle velocity:	*777mps (2550fps)*
Maximum range:	*2000m (6561ft)*
Effective range:	*800m (2624ft)*
Entered service:	*1997*

M4 CARBINE

The M4 Carbine is essentially the M16A2 but with a collapsible stock. Because of its compact size, it is ideally suited to special operations work, a capability that was further enhanced with the introduction of the M4 Carbine Special Operations Peculiar Modification Accessory Kit. This includes an x4 day scope which allows soldiers to judge range and then fire more accurately beyond 300m (984ft). In addition, the Reflex sight is designed for close-range engagements. Only one sight, as opposed to the normal two sights, needs to be aligned with the target. The shooter can keep both eyes open while using this accessory, allowing more rapid engagements. The visible laser places a red aiming dot on the target, while the infrared pointer/illuminator is used at night and can only be seen with night-vision goggles. The visible light is a high-intensity rail-mounted flashlight and is best used in buildings.

The forward hand grip helps to stabilize the weapon and also helps keep the hand away from the hand guards and barrel, which become hot during use. The sound suppressor is essentially defensive by reducing noise and flash, thus making it more difficult to discern the direction of fire. To accommodate these accessories, a series of rigid grooved rails replaces the normal hand guards. The M4 has seen extensive service with US élite units.

SPECIFICATIONS

Manufacturer:	Colt
Type:	carbine
Calibre:	5.56mm
Cartridge:	5.56 x 45mm NATO
Length:	757–838mm (29.8–33in)
Length of barrel:	370mm (14.57in)
Number of grooves:	6
Weight:	2.64kg (5.8lb)
Cyclic rate of fire:	700rpm
Practical rate of fire:	150rpm
Operation:	gas
Magazine capacity:	20 or 30
Fire mode:	semi-, full-auto, three-round burst
Muzzle velocity:	948mps (3110fps)
Maximum range:	1500m (4921ft)
Effective range:	550m (1804ft)
Entered service:	1982

M40

In April 1966, the Remington company in the United States offered the US Marine Corps (USMC) its sniper rifle, which was based on the Model 40XB target rifle. Some 800 rifles were initially offered under the designation M40 Sniper Rifle, and Remington eventually built a total of 995 for the Marines.

In the 1970s the initial M40s began to wear out, and so the Marines began to rebuild their inventory into the M40A1 configuration. The M40A1 was built around the same 700BDL actions, but with a polymer stock and a different scope. In 1996, the US Marines started on the design for the replacement of the M40A1, and the result was the M40A3. The latter uses a Remington 700 short action, with a steel floorplate assembly and a new trigger guard. The stock is a new McMillan A4, with adjustable cheek plate and length of pull. As the M40A1s rotate in for service and repair, they are replaced by M40A3 models. The M40 has no iron sights because the telescopic sight is fitted as standard.

All M40A3s are built by USMC armourers at Quantico, Virginia. The M40A3 is extremely accurate, very rugged and is designed from the ground up to be a superb sniper rifle. Combined with the new M118LR ammunition, it creates a system that is ranked with the best in the world.

SPECIFICATIONS

Manufacturer:	Remington
Type:	sniper rifle
Calibre:	7.62mm
Cartridge:	7.62 x 51mm NATO
Length:	1117mm (43.9in)
Length of barrel:	610mm (24in)
Number of grooves:	4
Weight:	6.57kg (14.45lb)
Cyclic rate of fire:	n/a
Practical rate of fire:	10rpm
Operation:	bolt
Magazine capacity:	5
Fire mode:	single shot
Muzzle velocity:	777mps (2550fps)
Maximum range:	2000m (6561ft)
Effective range:	800m (2624ft)
Entered service:	1996

M60

The M60 machine gun has been the US Army's general purpose machine gun since 1960. It fires the standard NATO 7.62mm round, has a removable barrel which can be easily changed to prevent overheating, an integral, folding bipod, and can also be mounted on a folding tripod.

The M60E2 is a modified M60 designed for coaxial tank mounting. The butt and fore-end are removed and an extension tube is fitted to the barrel, and another to the gas cylinder, which vents the operating gases outside the tank.

The M60E3 version manufactured by Saco is a lightweight, air-cooled, portable or tripod-mounted weapon designed for ground operations. It is gas operated with a fixed headspace and timing which permits rapid changing of barrels. The M60E3 also has a receiver-attached bipod which easily deploys for stability. It has ambidextrous safety, universal sling attachments, a carrying handle on the barrel, and a simplified gas system that does not require safety wire to prevent loosening. However, the lightweight barrel cannot sustain a rapid rate of fire of 200 rounds per minute or over without a catastrophic failure of the barrel.

The E4 version is a further improvement on the E3. It features a strengthened bipod, an improved feed system to give better belt lift, an improved flash eliminator, and an optical sight mount integrated into the receiver cover.

SPECIFICATIONS

Manufacturer:	*Bridge & Inland*
Type:	*general purpose machine gun*
Calibre:	*7.62mm*
Cartridge:	*7.62 x 51mm NATO*
Length:	*1105mm (43.5in)*
Length of barrel:	*560mm (22.04in)*
Number of grooves:	*4*
Weight:	*10.51kg (23.21lb)*
Cyclic rate of fire:	*550rpm*
Practical rate of fire:	*200rpm*
Operation:	*gas*
Magazine capacity:	*metal link belt*
Fire mode:	*full-auto*
Muzzle velocity:	*865mps (2838fps)*
Maximum range:	*3000m (9842ft)*
Effective range:	*1000m (3280ft)*
Entered service:	*1960*

M82A1

The Barrett M82A1 is an anti-material/sniper rifle, and it is supremely suited for these jobs. The original weapon was designed by Ronald Barrett in the 1980s, and was one of the first semi-automatic rifles chambered for cartridges normally reserved for heavy machine guns. The Barrett was used in the 1991 Gulf War for sniping, and to destroy landmines from a safe distance.

The Barrett is a large rifle, with a total length of 1549mm (61in) and a weight of 13.4kg (29.48lb), which fires the powerful .5in BMG cartridge from a 10-shot magazine. Its layout is conventional, with the magazine in front of the trigger guard, and a mounting for a scope on top of the receiver. The action is of the Short Recoil type, i.e. the recoil of firing the weapon moves the locked barrel/bolt assembly about 53.5mm (2.5in) to the rear, after which the bolt rotates and continues to travel backwards while the barrel stops. The bolt then travels forward again, strips a round out of the magazine and chambers it. Then the bolt rotates again, locking it and the barrel, and the closed assembly moves 53.5mm (2.5in) forward again, thus ending the cycle.

The Barret is truly an awesome weapon, which can disable light-skinned vehicles as well as enemy personnel at greater ranges than other sniper rifles.

SPECIFICATIONS

Manufacturer:	*Barrett*
Type:	*anti-material/sniper rifle*
Calibre:	*12.7mm*
Cartridge:	*12.7 x 99mm*
Length:	*1549mm (61in)*
Length of barrel:	*737mm (29in)*
Number of grooves:	*8*
Weight:	*13.4kg (29.48lb)*
Cyclic rate of fire:	*n/a*
Practical rate of fire:	*10rpm*
Operation:	*recoil*
Magazine capacity:	*10*
Fire mode:	*semi-auto*
Muzzle velocity:	*853mps (2798fps)*
Maximum range:	*3000m (9842fps)*
Effective range:	*1500m (4921ft)*
Entered service:	*1983*

M95

The Barrett Model 95 is a relatively small, lightweight 12.7mm-calibre rifle with an emphasis placed on accuracy and durability. The robust bullpup design results in a compact rifle with no sacrifice with regard to accuracy or velocity thanks to its cryogenically treated 737mm (29in) barrel (which is the same length as the Model 82A1). Recoil is reduced by the dual-chamber muzzle brake and specially designed recoil pad.

The rugged three-lug bolt of the Model 95 locks rigidly into the barrel extension to accommodate the widest variety of factory ammunition loads. The adjustable bipod may easily be detached by removing a single quick-release pin. The heavy, smooth barrel has a massive muzzle brake.

The Model 95 is designed to mount a variety of telescopic sights, and with good ammunition this combination results in excellent accuracy. The Model 95 may be disassembled for cleaning without tools, which makes it ideal for field use (Barrett has ongoing research and development contracts with the US Army's Special Forces and US Marine Corps for the development of product improvements to enhance the capability of fielded equipment). The Model 95 is another excellent sniper rifle from Barrett, a company renowned for producing rifles of the highest quality and performance.

SPECIFICATIONS

Manufacturer:	Barrett
Type:	sniper rifle
Calibre:	12.7mm
Cartridge:	12.7 x 99mm
Length:	1143mm (45in)
Length of barrel:	737mm (29in)
Number of grooves:	8
Weight:	10kg (22lb)
Cyclic rate of fire:	n/a
Practical rate of fire:	10rpm
Operation:	bolt
Magazine capacity:	5
Fire mode:	single shot
Muzzle velocity:	853mps (2798fps)
Maximum range:	3000m (9842fps)
Effective range:	1500m (4921ft)
Entered service:	1995

M99

The Barrett Model 99 (Big Shot) Rifle is the latest addition to the Barrett family of 12.7mm-calibre rifles. First shown in 1999, the extremely accurate Big Shot has captured the attention of long-range 12.7mm-calibre shooters around the world. What makes the Big Shot unique is its rugged aluminium alloy receiver, with cantilevered barrel and multi-lug bolt design. The interior of the 838mm (33in) barrel is machined to the same exacting specifications of all Barrett products, and inspected for dimensional compliance with state-of-the-art air gauging. The exterior of the barrel is unfluted to maximize the rigidity and thus the accuracy of the system.

Accurate scope mounting on the Big Shot is facilitated by the M1913 Picatinny (modified Weaver) Rail that is formed as an integral part of the receiver. This rail has become the new industry standard and allows easy removal and re-attachment of scopes with minimal effect on zero. The simple, straightforward design of the Big Shot makes disassembly easy and maintenance very straightforward. Three quick-release pins secure the trigger and bolt guide to the receiver. When these pins are removed the entire rifle can be easily disassembled for cleaning and lubrication. A fourth quick-release pin removes the adjustable bipod to accommodate bench-rest shooting.

SPECIFICATIONS

Manufacturer:	*Barrett*
Type:	*sniper rifle*
Calibre:	*12.7mm*
Cartridge:	*12.7 x 99mm*
Length:	*1280mm (50.39in)*
Length of barrel:	*838mm (33in)*
Number of grooves:	*8*
Weight:	*11.36kg (25lb)*
Cyclic rate of fire:	*n/a*
Practical rate of fire:	*10rpm*
Operation:	*bolt*
Magazine capacity:	*unknown*
Fire mode:	*single shot*
Muzzle velocity:	*unknown*
Maximum range:	*unknown*
Effective range:	*unknown*
Entered service:	*1999*

MAC 10

Designed by Gordon Ingram around 1970, this submachine gun was first manufactured by the Military Armament Corporation (MAC), hence its designation, and it was designed to be smaller, more compact and less expensive than other comparative designs. It is one of the most reliable submachine guns in existence. Firing from an open bolt which when closed partially wraps around the barrel, the entire weapon is made from pressed steel plate. It has a phenomenal rate of fire – as high as 1280rpm – and an entire magazine of 32 rounds can be emptied in under 1.5 seconds!

The MAC 10 also became well known for the numerous suppressors that were made for it. These were highly effective, and wrapped with cloth they were excellent for holding on to. The MAC 10 is small enough to be fitted into a briefcase; indeed, several kinds of briefcases were made that not merely allowed the concealed carrying of a silenced MAC 10, but the actual firing of one from inside the briefcase (Heckler & Koch have copied this to allow their MP5K to be fired from a specially designed briefcase). Though the standard magazine for the MAC 10 holds 32 rounds, many different versions can be found.

The MAC 11 is a slightly smaller version, being chambered for the 9mm Short cartridge.

SPECIFICATIONS

Manufacturer:	*Military Armament Corporation*
Type:	*submachine gun*
Calibre:	*9mm*
Cartridge:	*9mm Parabellum*
Length:	*298–559mm (11.73–22in)*
Length of barrel:	*146mm (5.75in)*
Number of grooves:	*6*
Weight:	*2.72kg (5.98lb)*
Cyclic rate of fire:	*1280rpm*
Practical rate of fire:	*300rpm*
Operation:	*blowback*
Magazine capacity:	*32*
Fire mode:	*semi-, full-auto*
Muzzle velocity:	*380mps (1200fps)*
Maximum range:	*150m (492ft)*
Effective range:	*50m (164ft)*
Entered service:	*1971*

STONER 63

Though they are no longer in service, the weapons of Eugene Stoner warrant a mention because they laid the foundations for many modern small arms. The Stoner 62 weapon system was based on the 7.62mm NATO cartridge. However, the design was interrupted when it became apparent that the United States was moving over to the 5.56mm round. The new design was then updated to the 63 system, which contained six separate but integrated weapon configurations: carbine, rifle, magazine-fed light machine gun, belt-feed light machine gun, medium machine gun and a fixed machine gun for vehicle mounts.

The Mk 23 (XM-207) was the only one of the designs to see combat, being used by US Navy SEAL teams in the Vietnam War in the 1960s.

Most SEAL Stoners were of the belt-fed, light machine gun variety, such as the Stoner 63A Commando (which had a shortened barrel). The gun used either a 150-round drum that attached beneath the gun and fed from the left, or a 100- or 150-round plastic box that mounted sideways beneath the gun and fed from the left.

In the field Stoners required diligent cleaning, lubrication and inspection of parts. A variation of the Stoner machine gun lives on today with the FN M249 belt- and magazine-fed squad automatic weapon (SAW).

SPECIFICATIONS

Manufacturer:	Cadillac Gage Corporation
Type:	light machine gun
Calibre:	5.56mm
Cartridge:	5.56 x 45mm M193
Length:	1029mm (40.24in)
Length of barrel:	551mm (21.69in)
Number of grooves:	4
Weight:	5.65kg (12.43lb)
Cyclic rate of fire:	700rpm
Practical rate of fire:	200rpm
Operation:	gas
Magazine capacity:	30 or metal link belt
Fire mode:	full-auto
Muzzle velocity:	990mps (3250fps)
Maximum range:	2653m (8704ft)
Effective range:	1000m (3280ft)
Entered service:	1965

INDEX

Picture Credits

All photographs The Robert Hunt Library except the following:

API: 121, 151, 156, 158, 160.
Barrett Firearms: 184, 185, 186.
FN Herstal: 105, 107, 108, 109, 110, 111, 112, 113.
Heckler & Koch: 122, 123, 124, 125, 126, 127, 128, 129, 130, 131, 132, 133, 134, 135, 136, 137, 138, 139.
Ian Hogg: 10, 11, 12, 13, 15, 26, 29, 30, 32, 33, 34, 37, 41, 43, 47, 50, 52, 53, 54, 55, 56, 57, 60, 61, 64, 65, 69, 71, 72, 73, 74, 85, 86, 89, 90, 92, 93, 94, 97.
MPL: 120, 148, 182.
Private collection: 101, 103, 147, 149, 152, 153, 154, 155, 161, 164, 170, 171, 175, 181, 187.
Sako Ltd: 115, 116, 117.
SIG: 172, 173, 174.
Singapore Technologies Kinetics: 165, 166, 167.
Steyr-Mannlicher AG: 99, 100, 102, 104.
Tim Ripley: 140.
TRH Pictures: 17, 19, 21, 24, 31, 36, 42, 49, 51, 62, 66, 67, 79, 84, 87, 88, 106, 114, 118, 141, 142, 143, 144, 145, 146, 150, 157, 159, 162, 163, 188.
US Department of Defense: 119, 168, 169, 176, 177, 178, 179, 183.
Use by permission from Remington Arms Company, Inc.: 180.